1.96

TWO-WHEELED THUNDER

By William Campbell Gault

TWO-WHEELED THUNDER

By William Campbell Gault

E. P. DUTTON & COMPANY, INC., NEW YORK

Published simultaneously in Canada by Clarke,
Irwin & Co., Ltd. of Toronto

Library of Congress Catalog Card Number: 62-7832

FOR CHUCK BARKER

TWO-WHEELED THUNDER

Chapter 1

THE NAME of my town is Dune. It's a desert town and you won't find it on many maps; the population is too small. There isn't even a motel, though Mrs. Wilson takes in tourists. There isn't an automobile dealer in town. The only automobile repair work is done at Ben and Ed's Filling Station and they won't take on anything heavier than a valve job, unless it's an emergency.

But we had a bicycle shop, Mr. Ellender's, and Mr. Ellender also sold a few motorcycles. He was a fierce old man, thin as a racing bicycle, and always grumbling about something. But he was Jerry's uncle so he was usually tolerant of Jerry and me.

Jerry's my buddy, Jerry Wilson. His mother is the Mrs. Wilson who takes in tourists. Mr. Wilson is dead; he was dead before I knew Jerry, and I've known Jerry ever since I could play outdoors alone.

There isn't too much to do in a town the size of Dune except watch television, and both Jerry and I were too young to be spectators when we could be participants.

As Mr. Ellender used to say: "Television is *secondhand* living. That's for people over eighty."

So Mr. Ellender's bicycle shop, with the repair shed behind it, became our playroom, Jerry's and mine. In

13

that shed we took our bikes apart and put them together again. It was certainly more fun than watching television.

And then one day Mr. Ellender sold a new motorcycle to a rider from Oasis City, taking in as trade an old one-cylinder Harley-Davidson that had been in a wreck.

The front fork was cracked beyond repair and the chain was missing, but the engine hadn't been damaged. Mr. Ellender set it back in the repair shed, planning to check it over in the not-too-close future.

Jerry asked him if we couldn't work on it, just for practice. His uncle grumbled a little, but we waited through that. And then he said, "All right. But you get into anything that looks difficult, you come to me before you take it apart. Understand?"

"Of course, Uncle Charley," Jerry said, in that polite way he has. "You know I would." He winked at me.

"Hmmmph!" Mr. Ellender said. "You don't fool me, Jerry Wilson. You think you know all there is to know about that Harley, right this second."

"It's not very complicated," Jerry said, "an old one-lunger like that."

"Hmmmph," Mr. Ellender said again. He looked at me. "Tom, you stay with him. And if he seems to be heading for trouble, you come get me."

I nodded.

Mr. Ellender looked at Jerry. "You don't work on that alone, not for a minute. You work on that machine *together*. Is that clear?"

"Of course," Jerry said. "Tom and I do everything together."

"Good thing," Mr. Ellender commented, and went back to his front shop and showroom.

Jerry smiled sadly. "He doesn't trust me, does he? But he trusts you. Now, why?"

"You've got it wrong," I said. "It's only that he worries about you. He doesn't worry about me, because I'm not his favorite and only nephew. But you are. He's been mighty patient with us, Jerry."

"Sure," Jerry said. "He's a great guy. Do you think we could pick up a used fork in Bakersfield?"

"I doubt it," I said, "but we could advertise for one in *Cycle* magazine, as soon as we find out the year and model number. Man, it's an ancient chariot, isn't it?"

Jerry nodded slowly, feasting his eyes on it. Finally he said, "But it's a lot better than a bike, you'll have to admit."

In his mind, it was already his.

We didn't worry about the chain; Mr. Ellender could cut that to any length needed. The fork was our big worry. We sent in an ad to *Cycle* and started to dismantle the whole machine.

For some reason, the motorcycle doesn't interest as many young people in this country as the automobile does. I don't understand it. It's much more economical to own and operate and it makes more sense as transportation. Have you ever stopped to realize that even a *small* car weighs twenty times as much as its driver? All that horsepower is needed to move the machine; only *one twentieth* of it is needed to carry the person it was designed to carry.

A passenger vehicle, to my mind, should be designed to carry the passenger. If you want to carry a lot of unnecessary steel around, it's better to buy a truck and go into the steel-carrying business. At least, that way you get paid for it, instead of paying.

Well, maybe if there had been some automobile dealers in Dune, I wouldn't be talking this way. But I guess the rate the compact cars are selling these days indicates that a lot of other Americans are beginning to think about all that useless and expensive weight.

Don't go away; the lecture's over.

So we took that old Harley apart, Jerry and I, mostly Jerry. And only once did I think it might be wise to call in Mr. Ellender; that was when Jerry wanted to take the transmission apart.

Mr. Ellender helped us with that and we went on. We washed all the bearings and gummed gears in kerosene, cleaned up and relubricated everything before we began putting her back together again.

We worked slowly and were only about half finished when we received an answer to our ad.

A junk dealer in Los Angeles had a fork he would sell for twelve dollars. We took the letter in to Mr. Ellender.

"Twelve dollars—" he grumbled. "I'd be lucky to get twenty-five for the machine. Twelve dollars— The man must be crazy!"

"There probably aren't many forks like that

around," Jerry pointed out. "That Harley isn't worth *anything* without the fork."

Mr. Ellender smiled. "Isn't it, now? It's worth something to a man who has a fork but no machine. I'll bet it's worth something to that fellow in Los Angeles."

Jerry looked crestfallen.

Mr. Ellender continued to smile. "How much money have you, Jerry?"

He sighed. "Three dollars and ninety cents."

Mr. Ellender looked at me.

"I've saved almost five," I said. I had a paper route at the time.

"Okay," Mr. Ellender said. "Offer the man seven dollars for the fork; tell him it's all you have. Tell him you'll pay the freight. I here and now bequeath you boys that Harley."

I think Jerry had assumed that motorcycle was going to be *his*, not *ours*. He looked at me and I studied his face for any signs of disappointment. He was grinning happily.

"I knew we'd get it, Tom," he said. "Uncle Charley may be grouchy, but he's generous."

"Humph!" Mr. Ellender said.

So we offered the Los Angeles dealer seven dollars, explaining in the letter the state of our finances. And three days later we had our fork, sent on the afternoon bus from the big city.

It was more work than we thought it would be; I was late for dinner that night.

My dad looked at the grime under my nails, the dirt even lanolin wouldn't remove, and guessed, "The fork came."

I nodded.

"And now that contraption is ready to ride."

I took a breath. "Not quite. Tomorrow, Jerry's going to help me with my route and then we'll finish the work."

"You've never ridden a motorcycle," he said. "Or have you?"

I shook my head. "It's the same as a bike, though. There's nothing to riding a motorcycle."

He sighed and looked at my mother. My mother said, "Tom, that thing has both of us worried. We've been talking it over." She paused.

I thought my heart was going to stop. All that work . . . and now maybe . . . ?

But she said, "You're a steady boy. You're honest. All we ask is your promise that you'll be extra careful every second you're on that machine."

"I promise."

"And," my dad added, "that you won't drive it at night for at least a month. There's no battery, is there?"

"Only a magneto," I admitted.

"I can imagine," he said, "what kind of lighting *that* will give you. Too slow and you have no light. Too fast and you burn out the bulb. I want to check that light before you ride at night."

He didn't have to. Mr. Ellender had already

checked it and we had our orders from him—*no* night riding.

Well, summer was coming on and the days were getting longer, so it really wasn't much of a restriction. We rode the Harley through the streets of town and on the highway that led to Oasis City.

And then one afternoon Jerry said, "Why don't we try it in the sand?"

There was plenty of that around, sand and sage in every direction as far as the eye could see.

"You're punchy," I said. "Why in the sand?"

"Practice," he said. "Look how many meets are held in the desert, all that racing in the sand, scrambles and marathons and—"

"Racing?" I said. "Are we going to enter some races? With *this?*" I shook my head. "What would we race against, tricycles?"

"You—!" he said and sighed. "You're such a—a realist!"

I laughed and he laughed, too.

And then, seriously, he said, "Tom, this is just a start, isn't it? We're going to go up from here, aren't we?"

"In my dreams, yes," I said. "About every other night, I dream of a big twin, and winning a hare and hounds, taking an AMA Championship in my hundred-dollar leather suit—" I laughed again. "Then I wake up and try to figure how to get all that on a paper route. You know, Jerry, the way I figure it, every family in this town would have to take two thousand copies of my paper every day. I'd have to deliver the route in a truck."

"That's your fault," he said, "for waking up. I'd rather dream." He kicked our old pony into life and said grimly, "Desert, here I come!"

He had a good start by the time he hit the sand, almost a hundred yards of asphalt, and the little one-lunger was moving smartly. For the first thirty feet or so in the sand, the front wheel was high, because of the thrust the asphalt had afforded him.

And then the front wheel settled in the heavy sand and the cycle stopped abruptly.

But Jerry didn't. Jerry went sailing over the handlebars, plowing a furrow in the sand until he finally tumbled into some sagebrush. I ran over, my heart hammering, but he was up and grinning by the time I got to him.

"Not enough power," he explained. "It takes more than this baby has to keep that rear wheel digging and that front wheel high. We'll have to wait."

We'll have to wait. . . . His future was planned, now, a motorcycle future. But *we*—? Was he planning mine, too? I went over to pick up the bike as Jerry opened his shirt to let the sand out.

His right forearm was scratched from the sagebrush. I said, "We'd better get some iodine on that."

We, again. He had me doing it. For a car, *we* might be all right. But though a motorcycle will carry two passengers, three with a sidecar, it has this in common with the horse—it's more fun with only one person aboard.

That hot April afternoon, as I trundled that old Harley across the sand to the hard surface again, I realized that if we continued the way we seemed to be headed, we'd get the big machine some day. We'd each get one. And that would make us competitors.

Jerry came up to walk alongside of me, carefully brushing the sand from his scratched arm.

He's competitive, I thought. *He's not petty or cheap or mean, but man, how he hates to lose!*

"What are you thinking about?" he asked.

Maybe I blushed. At any rate, I said, "I've been thinking about how competitive you are."

"So—? Isn't everybody?"

"Not always as much as you are. I was thinking if we keep going the way our dreams are, we'll wind up with a big twin each."

"And compete, probably," he admitted. "So—?"

"So all these childhood years of building up a solid friendship," I went on, only half joking; "so the first time I trim you in a meet, good-by, Tom!"

He laughed. "You're crazy. You know what's wrong with that?"

"Tell me."

"You wouldn't win," he said lightly. "How can I be a bad loser if I don't lose?"

"Maybe I'd have a faster machine."

He gripped my shoulder. "Maybe. I wouldn't mind losing to a faster machine. *Anybody* can lose to a faster machine." He chuckled. "We're Tom and Jerry, remember? We took the blood-brother oath."

And we both laughed. We'd taken that oath, solemn as owls, when we were both eight in order to join a club started by a breakfast-food manufacturer. It had been a standing joke since.

I can still remember that scene in the desert, that hot April afternoon, and the dialogue. I couldn't have called it better with a crystal ball.

Chapter 2

MY DAD is an engineer and he worked for an air-conditioning firm whose offices were in Los Angeles. He had this whole county as his territory and lived in Dune because it was almost in the exact center of the county.

There were bigger towns not too far away, but I was always glad he had chosen Dune. Because if he hadn't, I wouldn't have met Jerry Wilson. And if I hadn't met Jerry, the chances were I would never have become interested in motorcycles.

Those two-wheeled monsters have given me enough grief, but they've given me even more pleasure and enough thrills to last any reasonable man a lifetime.

The other day Jess Thomas in an unblown forty-inch Triumph averaged 214.47 mph for a two-way run at Bonneville Salt Flats. Four-wheeled gargantuas have gone a lot faster, I'll grant you, but how would you like to be on two wheels at two hundred and fourteen miles an hour? I guess you would have to label that a thrill.

Jess Thomas at Bonneville is a long way, I must admit, from Tom Manning, half-owner of an ancient Harley, in Dune, California. But knowing a road can lead to Bonneville or Daytona Beach makes the trip a lot more interesting, I think.

My dreams grew bigger but my income remained the same; there were only so many people in Dune who wanted to subscribe to the Oasis City *Bugle*.

That short and unhappy trip in the sand bothered Jerry. With only a little more power, he was sure, our tired old girl would have enough zip to keep digging. And a lot of meets, he explained gravely, were held in the desert.

We put in new rings, smoothed the ports and stepped up the compression. We found a hotter mag for sale cheap through one of the trade magazines. Mr. Ellender let us clean up his shop in order to earn enough to buy the mag.

With the higher compression, we used a gasoline of higher octane rating. That's one of the virtues in owning a cycle; the price of gasoline is almost immaterial, considering the mileage a cycle delivers.

When we finished, our machine had more zip. But something else happened at the same time that improved our desert traction. We had a freak rain that settled the sand.

For four days, until the sun dried it and the wind drifted it again, we had a circus with that pepped-up single, running our own noncompetitive scramble on a course we laid out with powdered lime.

We borrowed Mr. Ellender's stop watch and took turns timing each other. Jerry's best time for one lap on this course was thirty-five and a half seconds. The closest I came to that was thirty-six seconds, *I thought,* until we were cleaning up Mr. Ellender's showroom that night. And then, as he was dusting one of the cycles, Jerry said quietly, "Tom, I lied to you this afternoon."

I looked at him curiously. He wasn't looking at me. I asked, "About what?"

He still didn't look at me. "About that last lap of yours. You made it in *thirty-four* seconds."

I laughed. "I'm the champ, then."

He took a deep breath. "Man, I hate to lose. But I didn't think I'd ever lie in order to win."

"You didn't win by lying," I pointed out. "I had the best time, whether I knew it or not."

"Sure," he said, still not looking at me. "Wasn't that dumb of me? What kind of a creep am I?"

"You're a bad loser," I said frankly. "You'll get over it."

He looked at me, now. "How—?"

"By losing. The more you lose, the more practice you'll get. I hope you don't think you can go to your grave without losing a couple million times."

"I'll never get used to it," he said earnestly. "*Never!*"

I laughed again. "Wait. Wait and see."

The sand dried out and began to drift again and now we had a better comparative test of how much we had increased our mount's horsepower.

We had more power than before but not enough to give us any thrills, and only a minimum of experience.

The machine wandered though it remained upright; under acceleration it dug into the sand too deeply because of the narrow rear tire. We would need more machine than this to get desert scrambles experience.

To me, at the time, this wasn't important. Riding on the highway was enough fun for me; getting experience that might later be used in competitive riding was only a game we weren't equipped to play.

But Jerry was single-minded, his future charted. He was going to make his living from racing motorcycles. Well, a few years back, the FBI had been his choice and a year before that it had been anything connected with horses. So I smiled and agreed with him and wondered how long his enthusiasm would last.

And then something happened that brought me into the orbit of his enthusiasm. His uncle received four free tickets to a sport-car race that was being held at Oasis City, at the airport.

In conjunction with the meet, the Oasis City Cycle Club was running a motorcycle drag meet before the race. Jerry convinced his uncle the tickets should be used and Mr. Ellender didn't have much trouble convincing my dad that he should use the fourth ticket.

Until that Sunday, the only hot machines I had seen had been in the pages of motorcycle magazines. The biggest machine Mr. Ellender had on display was a five-hundred-cubic-centimeter sport twin, all the motorcycle I had assumed any man would ever want.

But at Oasis City, I saw a one-thousand-cubic-centimeter supercharged Daxton that made the sport twin look like a bicycle. A cubic centimeter is .0610 of a cubic inch, in case you don't know it, and sixty-one cubic inches of engine might not seem like much to our friends on four wheels. But you must remember motorcycles are designed to carry passengers, not impress the neighbors; there were no useless tons of steel burdening that sweet engine.

There was a twin-engine Triumph at the meet designed specifically for its only chore, a dragster designed for drags. That and the Daxton were the machines that wound up in the top eliminator final.

But there were other machines, still maintaining manufacturers' specifications, that had been tuned to their absolute peak; machines suitable for road or track, gleaming sweethearts that moved off the line like comets, smoking the rubber on their rear wheels, spanning the quarter mile in less time than it takes to tell it.

After that, the sport-car rally was dull to me, though about 60 per cent of the spectators didn't even arrive until the cycle drags were over.

So it must be the old story about one man's meat being another man's poison. The four-wheeled vehicle is still America's darling—for reasons that will never be clear to me.

Next to me in the small temporary stands, my dad said to Mr. Ellender, "I had no idea motorcycles could wind up like that."

"They're winding them up to fourteen thousand revs," Mr. Ellender said, and shook his head. "And *why?* The speed limit in this state is sixty-five miles an hour. There are *bicycles* traveling faster than that."

"Why—?" my dad said jestingly. "Charley, look at the eyes of those kids. Speed, speed, speed—that's all kids think about today."

Mr. Ellender was thoughtful. "You know, I'll be seventy-three next July and I can't remember a time when kids weren't interested in speed and *more speed.*"

My father's hand rested on my shoulder. I thought it trembled. He said quietly, "Tom knows *one* place speed doesn't belong, don't you?"

The highway, he meant. I nodded.

Mr. Ellender chuckled and said to my dad, "At my age, I figure I'm already going too fast toward where I'm heading." He sighed. "Well, it's a young man's world. It always was."

Jerry said, "And this is *my* world." He nudged me. "How about you, Tom?"

"I'm sold," I admitted.

I was then earning an impressive six dollars a week on the paper route and I always managed to spend that. The kind of machines we had watched today were not for lads making six dollars a week.

But I was getting too old for the paper route and summer was coming on. With luck, I might find a summer job in Dune. And, with sense, I might be able to save some money.

My luck wasn't bad. At Ben and Ed's Filling Station, Mr. Ben Schulte told me they could use a boy, both to watch the drive and clean up around the garage, a mechanically inclined boy, he emphasized.

Way back in the 'twenties, I had heard, Mr. Schulte had been a Tourist Trophy Champion in England, though he had lost all interest in motorcycles soon after that.

He told me that a dollar and a half an hour was as high as they could pay for summer work and I told him that was fine with me.

And then I had to ask, "Is it true, Mr. Schulte, that you used to race motorcycles?"

He nodded. "Why?"

"I—just wondered. I'm interested in motorcycles.'

"You'll get over it," he said. "I hope. They're murderous things. They should be outlawed." He took a breath. "And now, about your duties here, and your hours—"

He had closed the subject in a way that didn't invite my opening it again. I made a mental note to keep my mouth shut about motorcycles around Mr. Ben Schulte.

Cleaning up a garage may sound like dirty work. But there are cleaning tools and detergents in use today that make it a breeze. And it was the kind of work that kept me around engines; I was bound to learn how to handle tools better, how to organize repair work from watching Mr. Schulte and his partner, Ed Haskins.

Service was the key word at that station. That meant

courtesy and all the free attentions to every customer who drove up before the pumps, whether he wanted a tankful of gas or directions to Oasis City. I learned there are large numbers of unreasonable people in this world and extra courtesy is the surest way to avoid friction.

I also learned that some people are more than unreasonable; they are *impossible*. In those rare instances, I stood my ground and both of the partners supported my stand.

In other words, I learned the most obvious fact in the world—*nobody* can please *everybody*. But we certainly tried at Ben and Ed's.

The station was on the highway so our trade was not confined to the local citizens. And because the highway led to the Oasis City Cycle Club's desert-scrambles course, we received more than our share of motorcycle trade.

I noticed that Mr. Schulte always seemed to be busy with something else when a motorcycle pulled up to the pumps. That left Mr. Haskins or me to wait on them and it was usually I.

No service station will get rich selling gasoline to motorcyclists but I hurried out to the drive every time I saw one of them. Each of the machines had its virtues and its faults, and sometimes the riders would tell me what they thought could be improved on their mounts.

Harley-Davidson was the big AMA winner that year; the first four riders in annual point standings all drove Harleys. So far as I knew it was the only motor-cycle company still owned and operated by Americans. At Chicopee Falls, the Indian people had sold out to a British firm.

And, of course, the first motorcycle I had ever ridden was that antique Harley Jerry and I still owned and rode.

Mr. Ellender had decided Jerry was old enough now to receive a boost in wages, so Jerry, too, was saving money, though not at the rate I was.

And then, in July, we had a chance to sell our machine. Bud Briskin offered us seventy dollars for it—in cash. Bud, too, had been saving his money. I'd sold him my paper route and he had resold it at a profit.

If we didn't count the hours we had put into the cycle, seventy dollars meant a worth while profit for us.

But as Jerry said, "It makes pedestrians of us again. What do you think, Tom?"

"I think we're lucky," I told him, "to find a man with seventy dollars who wants a machine that old. We may never find another one."

So we had thirty-five dollars more in our respective hope chests, looking ahead to the better, bigger cycles we both wanted. Though it was sad, parting with our first love. And the first couple of days that Bud went chugging around town, I must admit to a small resentment. He was reaping the benefit of our labor.

Mr. Schulte said, "I see you got rid of that contraption."

"Yes, sir. For seventy dollars."

"Good riddance," he said.

In the background, I could see his partner grinning. I kept my face straight.

Mr. Schulte noticed the grin, though. He muttered something and went into the office. Mr. Haskins came over to where I stood. He was smiling.

He said, "If Ben ever breaks down and talks about the old days, you'll hear some stories. He was quite a rider in his time."

"Why is he so bitter about it now?" I asked. "An accident—?"

Mr. Haskins shook his head. "Ben was riding for the Acme people. And then other riders came along on faster machines and started to beat him." Mr. Haskins sighed. "Well, Ben is two things—he's very loyal and a terrible loser. Acme didn't have the machine to compete with the new ones, but Ben stayed with them. And got clobbered."

I was quiet, thinking of Jerry.

Mr. Haskins said, "That's most of the story. Ben also complains that the new riders coming up were a different breed; too many of them were roughnecks who didn't care about rules."

"The motorcycle customers we get don't look like roughnecks," I said. "They're about our friendliest customers."

"That's right," Mr. Haskins said quietly. "You see, Tom, the world changes but Ben doesn't."

I knew that Mr. Schulte wasn't the only one who

thought there were too many rowdies riding motorcycles. And they all had examples to prove their prejudices. Back in Columbus, Ohio, the American Motorcycle Association was working to change that public image. And out here in California, Floyd Clymer's Worldwide Cycle Club was working toward the same goal.

But neither the AMA nor the WCC was going to have any success without the 100 per cent cooperation of the more than half-million riders throughout the country.

The responsibility of keeping the greatest sport on wheels a clean and growing sport depended finally and completely on the man in the saddle.

Chapter 3

DON'T GET the idea from that antique Harley we had
that singles are all underpowered, small-engine machines. Indian makes singles of all sizes right up to
the power-packed six-hundred-cubic-centimeter overhead-valve Typhoon. All the singles made today have
enough zip to please any reasonable rider.

But both Jerry and I had our hearts set on two-
cylinder machines, though I hadn't decided what make
I wanted. Jerry was bound by simple family and em-
ployer loyalty to buy from his uncle. His uncle was a
Triumph dealer. That didn't mean Jerry would be
buying a Triumph, not if he bought a second-hand
cycle. And the way his bank account was growing, a
new machine seemed out of the question.

On a July afternoon, when the temperature under
the shaded portico at Ben and Ed's was one hundred
and fourteen degrees Fahrenheit, he came trotting
over from his uncle's shop, all excited about a Temple
twin his uncle had just taken in trade.

"Can't you get off?" he begged me. "Can't you come
over for a couple minutes to look at it?"

"Not right now," I told him. "Slow down, man. You
must be crazy, running in this heat."

He wiped his wet forehead with a piece of clean

34

waste and put a dime into the Coke machine. He took a deep swallow and said, "A Temple Tornado, only two years old, runs like a dream—oh, Tom, you *have* to come over *now*."

"In twenty minutes," I soothed him, "Mr. Schulte will be back from lunch and I'll come over. It's not going to evaporate, Jerry. Even this heat couldn't evaporate steel."

He finished the Coke and put another dime into the machine. "I'll bet Uncle Charley will let me pay him on time. I *want* that cycle, Tom."

"Remember how your mother feels about time payments, Jerry," I warned him. "Don't get too hopeful, now."

He finished half of his second Coke in one swallow. "I'm going to get it," he said grimly. "My mother won't care if I owe Uncle Charley."

I said nothing. There was a silence.

He was looking at me curiously. "You don't believe I'm going to get it, do you?"

I laughed. "I'd hate to be the person who had to say 'no' to you. I guess you'll get it all right."

Another silence. Then, "Hey, Tom—blood brothers?"

"Absolutely," I agreed.

"I'll let you ride it," he said. "I'm not chintzy, Tom."

"What's eating you?" I asked him. "Of course you'll let me ride it. You didn't have to say that."

He took a deep breath of the hot, dry air. "I was— oh, thinking that if you were getting it and I was still on foot—I don't know—I guess you don't think like I do, Tom."

"I'm as competitive as you are," I assured him.

"But you're a better loser," he said.

"Probably not, Jerry." I smiled. "Maybe you're just a louder loser."

He laughed. He went over to put another dime into the Coke machine.

"Three—?" I asked. "Three Cokes in three minutes?"

"Naw," he said, and handed me the bottle. "Drink on me, blood brother. And get over to the shop as soon as you can." He waved and trotted off.

What energy. . . . What a fireball. . . . What a competitor. . . . And what a bad loser! My buddy, Jerry Wilson.

Who's perfect?

Mr. Schulte came back in about fifteen minutes and asked if I had been to lunch yet. I told him I hadn't and he told me to go. I didn't think I was obligated to tell him I was going over to look at the Temple Tornado.

It was a sweetheart, five hundred cubic centimeters of first-class British engineering, an overhead-valve twin easily adaptable to flat track, road racing, scrambles or endurance runs, enameled in a glistening ice blue with silver trim and black frame.

"Why," I asked, "would a man want to trade in a mount like that?"

Mr. Ellender said, "Temple doesn't have much of a

dealer or service organization in this country. The man was worried about parts and repairs."

"I make my own repairs," Jerry said, "and I can get parts from the dealer in Los Angeles."

"You—?" his uncle said. He glanced at me and stared at Jerry. "Have you some weird idea, young man, that that is going to be *your* machine?"

"Natch," Jerry said blithely.

His uncle's voice was drier than the hot air outside. "I see. You have inherited a fortune recently, have you?"

"I've saved two hundred dollars," Jerry said, his voice less blithe. "I can owe you the rest."

"Huh!" his uncle said.

Jerry winked at me, but his face was tight. "Uncle Charley, haven't I been a big surprise to you lately? Haven't I been a model employee?"

"You've been a hard worker," his uncle admitted. "But you always are, when you want something as badly as you want a motocycle. Once you get it, what kind of a worker will you be?"

"Even better," Jerry promised. "Why, I might set new records of punctuality and perseverance and industrial output and—"

His uncle raised a hand. "Enough, enough. Words won't do it this time, Jerry Wilson. Your mother would skin me alive if I even let you *ride* that cycle."

"She let me ride the other one," Jerry argued.

"But she's been sleeping much better nights since you sold it," Mr. Ellender said quietly. "Now, Jerry, we won't discuss that Temple Tornado any more today. That's an order!"

Jerry seemed to freeze, standing there quietly, staring at his uncle. I could see his eyes mist. He's no crybaby, but he gets so worked up. . . .

I said, "See you later, Jerry," and got out of there.

At the Dune Diner, I ordered a triple chocolate malt and a tomato and bacon sandwich and tried to relax under the air conditioning my dad had sold them.

Ice blue and silver and black, British engineered, ready to go, go, go. . . .

Barney, the counterman, asked, "What are you dreaming about, Tom? Icebergs? Mountain snow?"

I smiled at him and shrugged.

From behind the griddle, Joe Richards said, "He's dreaming about that cycle he sold Bud Briskin."

I shook my head. "We got a good price for that."

Joe chuckled. "Did you? Bud sold it to Fred Mueller for a hundred dollars."

"You're kidding," I said.

Joe raised his right hand, palm forward. "I swear to you he did. Fred was just in here. He told me Bud had his eye on a bigger machine, a twin that Charley Ellender took in trade."

"Oh, no!" I said, startled.

Both Joe and Barney laughed. Barney said, "Now we know what you were dreaming about, that machine Bud wants. Right?"

"I was thinking about it," I admitted, "but not about buying it. Why, Jerry would have a fit if his uncle sold that machine to anybody else."

Barney set my sandwich in front of me and said drily, "Jerry has had fits before." He brought over my malt. "Be honest, Tom—you'd like to buy the machine yourself, wouldn't you?"

I thought for a second and then chuckled. "I can't afford to be honest. Jerry might be listening." I looked steadily at Barney. "And Jerry Wilson is my best friend."

Barney's face and voice were bland. "And I guess Joe, here, is mine. But both of us will have to admit, Tom, that no man is perfect, friend or foe, huh?"

"Right," I agreed. "I know at least three men in the county who make better malts."

Barney sniffed, Joe laughed.

"And two right in town," I added, "who make better tomato and bacon sandwiches."

And now Joe sniffed and Barney laughed and we changed the subject to baseball, where there was less friction. We were all Dodger fans.

Bud Briskin was a trader, a real wheeler-and-dealer, and if he had decided he wanted that Temple Tornado, Jerry's case looked even weaker than it had half an hour ago. It had been anemic enough then.

I went back to the station and back to work. The problem was Jerry's, not mine. Even if I had enough money to pay cash for that cycle, I wouldn't have bought it, now. I couldn't do that to Jerry.

It was one of my long days and my dad brought over my dinner about six o'clock. There was very little traffic on the drive so he sat with me while I ate.

I told him about Jerry and the Temple twin and what I'd learned at the Dune Diner.

My dad smiled. "In a couple years, you boys will look back on this time of your life and laugh at how serious you were about those silly motorcycles."

"Maybe," I admitted. "But as an engineer can you think of anything sillier in the transportation field than a five-thousand-pound car carrying a two-hundred-pound man?"

"A valid point," he agreed. "How about a twenty-five-hundred-pound car carrying *five* two-hundred-pound men?"

"Better," I said. "And how many miles do you drive a year?"

"About thirty thousand," he answered.

"And when," I went on, "did you stop enjoying it?"

He chuckled. "About fifteen years ago. Is driving supposed to be fun? It's simply a way of getting around."

I said nothing.

After a few seconds, he said, "Well, all right. It used to be fun. Maybe power steering and power brakes and too much chrome and all that useless overhang has taken the fun out of it. Or maybe that wasn't it, at all. Maybe I grew up."

I said nothing, smiling.

He grinned. He stood up and ruffled my hair. "You're crazy, Tom Manning. But there's a possibility the world's even crazier. It's not important; I know you're going to be all right."

At the doorway, he turned. "I've had a pretty good first half, this year. If this urge for a new cycle gets unbearable, let me know. Your credit's established, with me."

He drove away and it seemed lonely in the station, though there was plenty of traffic on the highway.

Sport cars and compacts were selling better every year in America, both of them designed to eliminate all unnecessary weight. Was the motorcycle the next logical step?

Not as family transportation, certainly. But think of all the families who had two cars. As a second "car," did the motorcycle make sense? I wasn't qualified to judge that. But it seemed clear to me that there were millions of Americans who would be adequately and economically served by two-wheeled transportation.

There were a lot of people in this country who were missing a lot of fun.

A little after seven o'clock, Jerry came to the station, driving Mr. Ellender's old Pontiac.

"If you're through at seven-thirty," he said, "I thought we could drive into Oasis City. There's a good movie at the Arlington."

"Okay. I can make it." I paused, studying him. "Why so glum? What happened?"

"Uncle Charley won't let me buy that cycle on time and my mother won't lend me the money."

I didn't voice the rumor I'd heard about Bud Briskin. I said, "How much more do you need? Maybe I can lend it to you."

He shook his head stubbornly. "I wouldn't take it. I'll get a cycle, don't you worry. And I won't buy it from Uncle Charley."

Again, I held my tongue. He was being unfair to his uncle, who had been more than fair with him. But I knew Jerry's moods; he was not at the moment open to reason. He didn't need a counselor now; he needed a friend.

"We'll both get cycles," I said. "Will you watch the drive while I get cleaned up?"

I don't remember now what the movie was. I do remember that Jerry was unusually quiet, staring at the screen. I don't think he was following the story line; he was buried in the blackest of moods.

But it still wasn't his low point, I'm sure. That must have happened next day when Bud Briskin came in to buy that Temple Tornado from Jerry's uncle.

Jerry was working at the time and the whole transaction took place when he was in the shop. I was glad I wasn't there to see *that*.

Chapter 4

THE ANNUAL Sagebrush Scrambles of the OCCC (Oasis City Cycle Club) was held on the third Sunday in July that year, less than a week after Bud Briskin had bought the Tornado.

Bud was only a Probationary Novice in the AMA, but he was entered in this meet. Some of the West Coast's finest Amateurs and Experts made the trek every year and Bud was the target of some rather disparaging jests at the Dune Diner.

He took it with a smile. As he explained, "The only way I can go from Probationary Novice to Novice is through experience. A man can't win until he learns why he loses."

One of the alleged wits present said, "Do us one favor, Bud. Don't tell anybody you're from Dune."

Bud shrugged and winked at me. He gave his attention to the hamburger he was eating.

"Wait until Jerry Wilson hears about this," the wit went on. "He'll have the last laugh yet."

I thought Bud's face tightened a little.

"Right, Tom?" the wit asked me.

"I don't follow you," I said.

"Yes, you do. You know Jerry's hot about Bud getting that cycle. You're Jerry's best friend."

I said evenly, "Jerry's my best friend, but he's not my only friend. I'm a friend of Bud's, too."

The witless wit laughed and Bud took a deep breath. I said, "Why don't we talk about something else?"

And from behind the counter, Barney said, "A good idea. Tom's a good friend and a loyal one, as I had reason to learn the other day. So let's all lay off the corny humor."

There was a silence for about five minutes after that. The sharp-tongued lad left and Bud looked over at me. There was a question in his eyes.

"Don't ask me, Bud," I anticipated him. "I haven't asked Jerry how he feels. I haven't seen him for three days."

"I waved to him, yesterday," Bud said. "He didn't wave back."

I said nothing.

"He couldn't have it," Bud went on. "So what difference should it make to him that I bought it?"

I shrugged. "Bud, one thing I've learned at the filling station is that you can't please everybody. Jerry can be unreasonable. I wouldn't say it here if I hadn't said it to his face. He'll cool off. He always does."

Until I'd voiced it, it hadn't occurred to me that Jerry hadn't been around the station for three days. Mr. Schulte was on vacation so my hours had been long and busy.

I still had twenty minutes of my lunch hour left; I walked over to the cycle shop.

Jerry was in back, putting a new tire on a bicycle.

"Where have you been?" I asked him. "Haven't seen you for three days."

His grin was tight. "I've been sulking. I'm a *baby*, right?"

"Now and then. Are you over it?"

He shrugged. "Why?"

"I thought, if we can stand the heat, we'd go and watch that Sagebrush Scrambles tomorrow."

"I wouldn't ask my uncle for his car," he said.

"My dad told me I could use our car. He might even go along." I paused. "Do you think your Uncle Charley would like to go?"

He shrugged again.

"Should *I* ask him?"

He smiled. "Would you? We've been maintaining a real chilly employee-employer relationship around here this week."

"I'll ask him," I said. "Jerry, look at me."

He looked up from the tire to face me squarely.

"Grow up," I said. "Your uncle has been a very good friend to *both* of us."

"I know, I know, *I know!* Don't lecture me, Tom. You're not telling me anything I don't know."

We stared at each other for a few seconds and then I smiled. "I'll ask your uncle. See you later, Jerry."

His uncle was on the walk in front, talking to the mailman. I waited until the mailman had gone on and asked, "Mr. Ellender, wouldn't you like to see how the Triumphs do in that Sagebrush Scrambles tomorrow?"

He looked up at the blazing sun and back at me.

"In this heat? Those Oasis City boys are crazy, running a desert meet in July."

"The weather man says tomorrow will be overcast," I argued. "A few clouds can make a big difference, Mr. Ellender."

He snorted. "Sure can. Might bring the temperature down to a hundred and five."

I said nothing.

"Who else is going?" he asked.

"Jerry," I said. "And my dad might go."

He frowned. "Jerry put you up to this? Is this his way of apologizing for a week of bad manners?"

"It was all my idea, sir," I said.

He looked up at the sun again. "Well, maybe— You know, Tom, Jerry's my favorite nephew, but for only one reason— I don't have any other nephews. He's certainly a stubborn, spoiled boy, isn't he?"

"He's single-minded," I said. "He's a hard worker. He's a loyal friend. He's usually cheerful. Nobody's perfect, Mr. Ellender, and especially at our age."

He looked at me skeptically. "Are you implying that at *my* age *I'm* supposed to be perfect?"

"Of course not, sir."

He chuckled. "All right, Tom, I'll—see about tomorrow. If there are some clouds up there in the morning— Well, I'll let you know then."

I don't know how motorcycling rates on attendance figures as a spectator sport, but as a *participant* sport it must be very high in the competitive field.

The Big Bear Cross-Country has over eight hundred

competitors each year and there were almost twelve hundred participants in the last Death Valley Road Run. I've never heard of an automobile race with twelve hundred entries, but automobiles need better footage than cross-country runs afford, of course.

There were only about a hundred entries in the Sagebrush Scrambles this year, but it drew a number of respected names. Bart Markel was there and Stuart Morley. And there was a good friend of Mr. Ellender's there—Triumph's ace, Johnny Burke.

I was glad it was an overcast day or Mr. Ellender wouldn't have been there. And if he hadn't been there, we wouldn't have met Johnny Burke.

Mr. Ellender introduced him to my dad, first, and then said, "And here are a couple of boys heading your way, I guess, Johnny. They're saving up for cycles. Tell 'em what a rough game it is."

Johnny smiled and said, "That wouldn't discourage them if they like it. I'm surprised a Triumph dealer would talk it down."

He had taken a first at Daytona, that year, and was leading in the point standings up to the middle of July. Daytona was a two-hundred-mile test; this was a real star. He had finished fifth nationally the year before and the big "5" was attached to the front of his machine.

It was less than an hour to race time, but he didn't hurry, talking with us, an easygoing, confident man who was here only because he enjoyed it. He reminded me of the amateurs and novices and purely pleasure riders who stopped in at the filling station.

It was a six-mile course the OCCC had laid out here, with some rough going near the foothills, including what amounted to a miniature hill-climb test in the final arroyo. There were tight right- and left-hand turns; there was a sweeping right-hand turn after a jump that promised the most excitement.

We drove out to a knoll where we could see this jump and also the finish line.

Some of the boys were using oil with a castor-oil base, and the smell of it was heavy on the warm breeze. Near the starting line, a few engines were running, biting the air with stacatto barks, sharp and choppy music.

Jerry's eyes were wide as headlights as he took in the scene from the knoll. Mr. Ellender looked at my dad and sighed. My dad grinned.

"What a show!" Jerry said. "You notice, Tom, there's not a clunker in that field. What a line-up!"

I nodded agreement. My gaze moved from the machines to the sage-dotted desert, to the low hills lying in front of the mountain, to the dry creek bed winding down from the pass in the mountains. It was a rugged test, this course. The check stand at the far end was plainly visible in the clear air, as was the finish-line check stand. The finish-line stand was a stop check for each lap. It was a ten-lap race, roughly sixty miles of every kind of traction imaginable. An automobile couldn't have traveled the first mile of it.

Down in the starting field, now we could see Johnny

Burke's black Triumph lining up and also a blue, silver and black Temple Tornado. The rider of this last was a stocky lad with a brand-new, shining crash helmet—Bud Briskin.

I saw Jerry staring that way. Some of the exultation went out of his face and he squinted toward the mountains.

The engines were starting; the bark of them reverberated off the hills to the west. A big forty-inch Norton Manxman was pulling up next to Johnny Burke now and Mr. Ellender said, "That's Red Dunn. He's a friend of Johnny's."

Even from here, the "4" on the front of the Norton was visible. A thought came to me—I wondered if Jerry would sit on the starting line and chat with me if I was wearing a four and he a five. It was a disloyal thought and I killed it.

Jerry said, "That Bud Briskin has his nerve, trying to compete in this kind of company."

I said nothing.

"Will he ever get clobbered," Jerry said. "Right?"

I shrugged. "It's all experience. He has to start somewhere."

"Huh!" Jerry said.

It was a good time to keep my mouth shut, but I thought something should be said. So I said it. "Bud thinks you're angry about his buying that machine. You're not, are you? Not any more."

Jerry's voice was tight. "Why shouldn't I be?"

I didn't answer.

But Mr. Ellender did. He said evenly, "You couldn't have it, anyway. Why shouldn't Bud buy it?"

This time it was Jerry who didn't answer. We were all silent; some of the magic had gone from the day. And then that quiet second was shattered with the racket of a hundred engines and the desert seemed to tremble as the tape snapped and the Sagebrush Scrambles got under way.

If you remember how tough it is to watch all the action in a three-ring circus, you can imagine the difficulty in trying not to miss any action in a scrambles. It was a hundred-ring circus; one hundred performers on the world's finest mechanical horses jockeying for position and clearance in a rugged sixty-mile test.

At the far end of the course, near the hills, the sand was mixed with clay and that surface was like macadam in July. The longest straightaway was in this hard stretch. It ended in a sweeping left-hand turn and a dip into the arroyo.

The entry point to the arroyo was narrow and the course was strange to all the riders. The first three to come out of that big straightaway were on heavyweight machines and they were bunched and barreling.

Gus Hendrix was leading and Gus went into that left turn too fast, sliding out wide of the arroyo entry point, though it was well marked.

The two riders behind had played it cagier; they cut to Hendrix's left under perfect control and disappeared from view. There was enough of a gap for Gus to loop back and follow them, but he was in second gear now, and they were logging.

We were all watching the arroyo exit point now. Red Dunn's big Norton came jumping out, his front wheel a foot off the ground, not more than two lengths ahead of an Amateur on a big Harley. I started to count.

I counted slowly to sixteen before Gus Hendrix came into view. A Hare Scrambles, I thought, doesn't mean the hare has to win, not if the hounds are smarter. In a scramble, the race is not always to the swift.

Both leaders made the jump well, landing with the rear wheel low, and came gunning into the right-hand turn toward us. They rocketed past and zoomed into the final straightaway, slowing exactly right for the first lap-check.

It wasn't until then I looked back at the field, already strung over a mile and a half of course.

And second from the end in that trailing procession was Bud Briskin on his Temple Tornado.

Jerry laughed. "What'd I tell you?"

"It's a ten-lap race," I said. "Bud's in fast company. But when an old campaigner like Gus Hendrix can be outfoxed by an Amateur, *anything* can happen."

Jerry sniffed. "What are you, Bud's lawyer?"

"He's a friend of mine. And of yours. Easy now, Jerry."

Jerry said tightly. "He's no friend of mine." A pause. "Are you?"

Both Mr. Ellender and my dad had overheard, and they were listening as I answered quietly, "I'll let *you* decide that, Jerry."

Another pause, longer, and then Jerry grinned sheepishly. He said, "Blood brothers, Tom."

"Right," I said. "Onward, with Crispie Crunchies!"

Probationary Novice Bud Briskin didn't disgrace Dune that hot and hectic afternoon. He finished fifth among the Novices, and I went threading through the crowd to congratulate him. Jerry didn't come along.

Bud looked as though he had put in a twelve-hour shift in a badly managed coal mine, but he grinned at me and gripped my hand hard. "Who won?" he asked.

"Johnny Burke," I said, "natch. You were fifth among the Novices."

"And forty-sixth in the run," he added. "Who cares about classes? Some of the lightweights beat me."

I smiled.

He smiled, too. "Okay. I'm a big mouth. Where's Jerry?"

"Around somewhere," I said. "Maybe he's—ah, lost in the crowd, or something—"

He nodded. "Sure." He shook his head. "I wish he'd grow up."

"Forty-sixth," I said. "That means over fifty riders finished behind you or didn't finish. The boys in the Dune Diner will show more respect now, I'll bet."

He said lightly, "They don't bother me. They're all friends. I hope you get your cycle soon, Tom. And thanks for coming over."

There were other friends from Dune coming over to congratulate Bud now; perhaps he wouldn't miss Jerry Wilson.

On the trip back, Mr. Ellender and my dad did most of the talking. Jerry was quiet and so was I. I was remembering all the excitement of the afternoon, the jumps, the spills, the expert manipulation of those first-class machines. It had been a great show.

We dropped Jerry and Mr. Ellender off at their house and Jerry still hadn't talked much.

My dad asked, "Did you and Jerry quarrel about something?"

"No. Why?"

"He was unusually quiet on the way home. What was that discussion about Bud Briskin?"

I told him the story of the Temple Tornado and the conversation in the Dune Diner.

My dad said, "Maybe Jerry was miffed because you went over to congratulate Bud."

I thought for a second and then agreed, "That could be it. Well, Jerry's a friend and Bud's a friend. What could I do?"

"Exactly what you did," he said. "But, Tom, be patient with Jerry. He has his faults, but he has a number of virtues, too. He's a good boy." A pause. "Can you get off work tomorrow afternoon?"

"I think so. Why?"

"I thought we could run into Oasis City together."

"Oh—? What's there?"

"A bargain," he answered. "Only a year old and in

perfect condition. It won't be there long. If you haven't enough money, as I told you the other day, I can lend you some."

"A motorcycle—? What kind, Dad?"

"A BSA Spitfire Scrambler," he said. "A sweetheart."

"And how," I said. "But that's strictly a competition machine, isn't it? It doesn't even have a headlight for road use."

"This one does," he said. "And a generator, too, and a voltage control unit. Think you can get off?"

"I'll sure try," I promised.

Chapter 5

IT WAS a sweetheart, all right, sapphire blue, chrome and black. It was a forty-cubic-inch twin with full race camshaft and high-compression pistons. Actually, it was the competition model of the BSA Super Rocket, the fastest-selling model they had, a road machine.

The headlight was quickly detachable for competitive riding; this machine was not really designed for touring or transportation.

Staring at it there in the BSA showroom, I thought of Jerry Wilson.

My dad said, "You're interested more in the sport than in transportation, anyway, aren't you?"

Was I? I hadn't completely decided until now. But now I thought of Sunday's Sagebrush Scrambles and admitted, "I guess that's right. I was—thinking of Jerry Wilson. Bud with that Tornado and now if I came home with this— Oh, brother!"

He laughed. "So—? You don't want it?"

I didn't answer. I only looked at him.

He laughed again. "We can swing it. Let's see if we can dicker a few more dollars off the asking price."

I drove it home. My only previous experience had been with that old machine we'd sold Bud and I al-

most didn't make it home. Because a competition engine was a frightening step above that. I put her into
first gear and twisted the throttle—and the front wheel
lifted a foot off the ground as the machine almost shot
out from under me.

I hit the rear brake hard; the front wheel came slamming to the ground and I almost went over the handlebars. I sat there, with a killed engine, my heart hammering, feeling like the dumbest lout in the world.

The dealer was in his doorway. He was laughing.
He said, "My fault, son. I thought maybe you were
used to that kind of power. Are you going to be all
right?"

I nodded, not looking at him. My dad had already
gone around in back to the parking lot; I was glad *he*
hadn't seen that ridiculous display.

I started the engine again and sat there, waiting for
Dad to pull out of the lot. I hadn't taken a demonstra-
tion ride because we were getting a new cycle guaran-
tee on the machine and the dealer had run the engine
for us.

I looked up and he was still standing in the doorway. I smiled. "It's a lot of machine, isn't it?"

He nodded. "Are you eighteen?"

"Yes."

"You have to be eighteen to compete in AMA meets,"
he said. "I have a feeling you'll be competing."

I nodded again.

His voice was quiet, almost too quiet to hear above
the sound of the engine beneath me. "Take it easy.
Your first year is the year you *learn,* not *win.* Learn

early and live to win later. Will you remember that?"
"I will."

And then our station wagon was coming out of the driveway that led to the parking lot and Dad waved and I waved back. And this time I started slowly, getting the feel of this Spitfire, finding her pulse, respecting her power.

It was a machine designed for the rough going, for scrambles and Tourist Trophy races, for cross-country competition. But there was a drag being run at Oasis City Sunday and I planned to enter it because it was limited to Novices and there would be no big names from Los Angeles or Bakersfield. Those boys were too rough for me and they all had equipment to match the course. My Spitfire would have to do for all the courses, including drags.

There is an opinion held by many in motorcycling that first-class scrambles riders do not make first-class racing riders and vice versa. I don't think it's true. To my mind, an all-around rider should be able to compete on any kind of surface.

In any event, it didn't apply to me because I wasn't first-class in *any* kind of riding. Not that July Monday I followed my dad's wagon home from Oasis City.

As we came into Dune, I sat a little straighter in the saddle. The boys at the *Dune Diner* now had a new target for their quips and I wanted them to know I was ready for them.

Mom was in the front yard, talking to Mrs. Wilson, when we pulled into the driveway.

Both she and Mrs. Wilson stared at the Spitfire as though it was a six-legged animal and Mrs. Wilson shook her head sadly. My mother laughed and said, "Well, I suppose if I had a daughter I'd have other problems just as serious. I hope you boys didn't pay over ten dollars for that contraption."

My dad winked at me and said nothing.

Mrs. Wilson said, "Heavens, when Jerry sees that—" She shook her head again. "Tom, does he have to see it right away?"

I didn't know what to answer.

In the uncomfortable silence, my dad came through. He said, "I'm sure Tom will let Jerry ride it. In a town this size, it's difficult to hide a Spitfire Scrambler."

I had to be at the station by four o'clock; it was now three-thirty. Mom was fixing me a sandwich, five minutes later, when Jerry came over. He came right to the kitchen.

"Where is it?" he said excitedly. "Where is it—in the garage? The garage door's closed."

"So open it and look," I said. "A Spitfire Scrambler."

"I know," he said. "I saw you when you rode past the shop." He went out quickly.

My mother sighed.

In a couple minutes, Jerry was back. "Brother! Man, won't that Bud Briskin turn green now. Oh, are you lucky!"

Envy in his voice, but not a trace of resentment. Jerry Wilson was not always an easy man to figure.

"I'm lucky," I admitted. "I—thought I'd try it in

the drag Sunday at Oasis City. It's not really a machine for that, though."

"Huh!" he scoffed. "In that field, you'll stand out like a diamond. You'll cream 'em, boy." He held a clenched fist up. "I'm going along and root for you."

My dad came in from the living room as Jerry said that and my dad added, "I'm going along, too."

My mother looked at him curiously.

"Don't jump to conclusions, honey," he told her. "It's an interesting sport."

"But a highly competitive business," she said.

He grinned at her. "That's the best kind." He took a deep breath. "I never planned to be a salesman when I went to engineering school."

Both Jerry and I were staring at my dad now, wondering what this conversation was about.

But my mother said quietly, "You'd better hurry, Tom, or you'll be late for work."

We were a close family, and this was the first time I had heard my dad complain about selling air conditioning. I didn't ask any questions then; I was due at the station.

I walked to work. I would be relieving Mr. Schulte and I wasn't quite ready to hear his probable comments about the Spitfire.

There wasn't much trade that evening so I cleaned up the lube room. It's not a job that requires complete mental attention; as I worked I thought about the Spitfire and also about the strange dialogue between my mother and father.

I was sure my father didn't intend to get a sales franchise from a motorcycle firm. He had said he hadn't planned to be a salesman. His engineering degree was helpful to him as an air-conditioning salesman but perhaps he wanted to use more of his education than that.

He was in the den when I came home around eight o'clock. He was working on some papers at his desk. I hesitated—and then went in.

He looked up, smiled, and said, "Questions?"

"One. What was Mom talking about before I went to work?"

He stared at me for a second, still smiling. Then he said, "Sit down, boy, and hear the sad story of a loser."

When I was seated, he said, "Twenty years and one month ago, I graduated from engineering school." He paused. "Valedictorian of my class. The man who stood second in that class was a man named Walter Devlin. I guess you've heard me speak of him before."

I nodded. "He runs Devlin Engines. Power mowers, outboards, scooters— Isn't he a millionaire?"

"Yes, I'm sure he is." My father paused. "He was a poor man, twenty years and one month ago, a man who had just finished working his way through engineering school." He paused again. "And I'd be a lot poorer today if I hadn't bought some Devlin Engine stock about twelve years ago." A third pause, a long one.

I said, "You should have gone in with him twenty years ago; is that what you mean, Dad? You were married, weren't you, your last year in engineering school?"

"You're a perceptive lad," he said. "Yes, I was married. But it doesn't follow that if I hadn't been I would have thrown in with Walter Devlin. Walter was always a—a lot less conservative financially than I was, despite his poverty."

"But he wanted you to go in with him," I said.

"He did. I thought about it for almost a week—and then turned him down."

"And now—?" I asked.

"At least four or five times a year," he went on, "ever since our school days, almost, Walter and I have met for lunch in Los Angeles. Last time we met, I brought up the subject of motorcycles, because of your interest in them. And he told me he had been thinking of them, himself, lately. He had some advanced ideas, naturally." My dad chuckled. "Walter is never short on those."

I took a big guess. "He wants to manufacture motorcycles. He wants you to work for him."

"*With* him," my dad corrected me. "He wants me to put up that Devlin Engine stock and a few other dollars I have salted away."

I said nothing.

My father said, "The current market value of that stock is ninety-three thousand dollars. That's a lot of money, isn't it, Tom? I'll bet you never figured I had *that* much of a nest egg."

I took a breath and continued to say nothing.

My father said quietly, "It cost me thirty-two hundred dollars twelve years ago. It has split four times in the twelve years and I put all my dividends back in.

I guess you could say Walter Devlin has done all right by this family, couldn't you?"

I nodded. "But look what he did for himself!"

He laughed. "Your mother's words, exactly." He rubbed the back of his neck. "I wish I weren't forty-three years old, Tom. I wish I were your age."

"You don't look old to me," I said. "You don't act old."

He stood up and stretched. "Thank you! Let's go and see if there's any ice cream left in the freezer."

"Good idea," I said. "But one question, first."

"Shoot."

"With over ninety-three thousand dollars in the kitty, at the young age of forty-three, how can you call yourself a loser?"

He grinned at me, his head cocked to one side. "I guess I'm not, son, unless I compare myself with Walter. But that's the rub—Walter and I have been competitive since the day we met." He sighed. "And now he wants me to pay for my chicken-hearted decision of twenty years ago. He wants me to risk *my* money, too."

There was some ice cream in the freezer, our favorite flavor, chocolate-almond. We ate in the kitchen and talked about the Dodgers and the Spitfire and the drag on Sunday. And I was never once conscious of the fact that my father was forty-three.

But I was now conscious of the fact that there was a world beyond my own, a world of adults and parents, that had problems just as mine had. I started thinking of my dad as a person instead of a combination first sergeant and checkbook.

I could understand why an engineer who led his class might feel that he was wasting his education as a salesman. But I could also understand my mother's reluctance to put twenty years of savings and capital gain into a competitive business to be shared by a wheeler-and-dealer like Walter Devlin.

Seeing both sides of a question may be intelligent but it certainly isn't very comforting.

I rode the new cycle to work next morning. I started at nine, and Mr. Schulte wasn't due until ten, so I parked the machine behind the tire rack where he wouldn't have to look at it while working the drive.

Mr. Haskins saw it as I drove in, and he grinned as I parked it out of sight. He said, "You mustn't let Ben scare you with that grumpy voice of his."

"The less friction, the better," I said. "Mr. Schulte doesn't scare me. He's been very patient with me."

Mr. Haskins chuckled. "In a week, he'll probably ask you if he can ride it. It's been a long time since Ben's seen a real competition machine like that one."

Mr. Schulte didn't see it until almost noon, when he was trying to find a retreaded tire for a customer. He stared at it for about ten seconds before resuming his search for the tire.

And after the customer had left he went back again to examine it more closely.

Mr. Haskins and I were working under the lift and Mr. Haskins said, "What'd I tell you? He's reliving his youth."

"He must have had an unhappy childhood," I said. "He's not smiling."

Mr. Haskins laughed and called out to his partner, "Some machine, eh, Ben? Twenty-five cents a ride. Get your tickets at the office."

Mr. Schulte looked up, shook his head, and went out on the drive to wipe off the pumps. And then a couple of cars drove in and we all had our hands full for the next few minutes.

When I got back to the lube room, Mr. Haskins was still on the drive and Mr. Schulte was working under the car on the lift.

"That's quite a cycle," he said quietly. "You could have bought a good used car for what that must have cost you."

"Probably," I admitted.

He sighed. "I guess I'm getting old, old and unreasonable. Well, you treat that machine with respect, boy. That's a bomb."

"Forty cubic inches of bomb," I admitted.

"Forty—" he said thoughtfully. "Forty inches—that's about six hundred and fifty cubic centimeters, isn't it?"

I nodded.

He sighed again and said again, "You treat that machine with respect, boy."

And I nodded once more.

At one o'clock, I went to lunch. I walked over to the Dune Diner and took a seat in front of the counter—and waited.

Barney said, "Hi," and from behind the griddle Joe said, "Hi," and I said, "Hi," and I still waited.

Finally, Barney said, "Well, Tom, what'll it be?"

I had been waiting for the barbs and I was almost disappointed. I said, "Cheeseburger and a malt."

My lunch was half eaten when Bud came in. "Hey, lucky," he said, "where's that Spitfire?"

"Over at the station," I told him.

He took the stool next to mine. "Wait for me. I'll eat fast. I'll walk back to the station with you. I have to see that baby."

Barney and Joe smiled but said nothing.

"Are you going to the drag Sunday?"

"Yup. I have to get a crash helmet first, though."

"Use mine," Bud said. And then he paused. "Wait —we might be in the same pair-off. That's a big machine, right?"

"A big twin, overhead valve," I said.

He grinned. "Hey, wouldn't that be something? We'll make Dune famous!"

Joe winked at Barney and Barney sighed.

Bud nudged me. "They're dying to say something, but they don't speak our language." He looked at Barney. "Are you—you *spectators* planning to make the big event?"

Barney yawned. "I doubt it. We planned to see the dog show in Bakersfield."

We were all laughing at that one when Jerry walked in. We weren't laughing at him, of course. We hadn't even seen him until he walked in.

But Jerry didn't know that and Jerry has too much

imagination. He gave us all one startled, indignant glare, turned around and walked out.

Bud and I were riders, now. Jerry, like Barney and Joe, was a *spectator*. That would never be enough for him.

Chapter 6

WHEN MR. ELLENDER's car stopped in front of our house Sunday morning I didn't expect to see Jerry. But he came walking up to the house with his uncle and he had a sheepish grin on his face. I hadn't seen him since that Tuesday scene in the Dune Diner.

He said, "I thought you and Bud were laughing at me. Barney told me how wrong I was."

I only looked at him.

"So, okay," he said. "I'm a creep; I should think better of a friend. Well, it's been a sour month."

I shook my head. "Jerry, you're always in a hurry. Slow down, man! You'll get your cycle."

"Sure," he said impatiently. "I know, I know! No lectures. Did you get a crash helmet?"

I nodded. "My dad brought it home Thursday. AMA approved, too."

"Oh, boy!" he said. "Let's see it."

He was over his peeve. And though he didn't relish being a spectator he was going to be a fan, this afternoon, rooting for Probationary Novice Tom Manning.

Blow hot, blow cold, Jerry Wilson. . . .

The OCCC had arranged the day's events as to motor classification, lightweight and heavyweight, but had made no distinction between regular and Probationary Novices. I would be up against some boys sure to be rated Amateur by the end of this season, and one or two who would eventually wind up as Experts.

My dad went around with Mr. Ellender, asking questions, studying the machines, absorbing information like a dry blotter. He was particularly interested in the BMW, the only machine there that used an automobile-type driveshaft instead of a rear chain. I had the feeling we were about to invest the nest egg.

I saw Bud Briskin in the staging area and he saw me but he didn't come over, probably because Jerry was with me.

All around us, the boys were tinkering with their machines, a really mixed group. There were the washed boys with their crew haircuts and their gleaming machines and there were the boys with the duckbill haircuts and noisy friends. This last gang had almost destroyed hot rodding until the NHRA had brought some sanity to that sport. I hoped the AMA would do the same for cycling.

A small hoodlum minority in any sport can make enough noise to convince an unthinking public that it is a rowdies' game.

My dad and Mr. Ellender were over talking to Bud Briskin now and Dad spent more time looking over that Temple Tornado than he had on all the other machines together.

When he came back, he said, "That's the company Walter is dickering with."

I stared at him. "Temple—? They're a British firm."

"They have an assembly plant here," my father told me. "And Walter has a British plant making his scooters. It wouldn't involve much more than an exchange of stock. We'd have the right to change the American Temple for our market; they could do the same to Walter's scooter. What do you think of that Temple?"

"It's a sweetheart," I said quietly. And asked, "Who do you mean by 'we'? You haven't said 'yes' to Mr. Devlin yet, have you?"

He grinned. "Only in my mind."

"And Mom—?" I asked.

He sighed. "She's certainly not sold a hundred per cent." He looked around at the machines near us. "I am. This kind of transportation makes sense to me."

"And don't forget the sport angle," I said. "It actually is what they call it—the greatest sport on wheels."

And then next to me, Jerry said, "Hey, look! Isn't that one of your bosses over there?"

We all turned toward the way he was pointing. And Mr. Ellender said, "Ben Schulte! I never thought I'd see *this*." He nudged my father. "Let's go over and heckle him."

They left and Jerry looked at me. "Nervous?"

I nodded. "And it's worse, now, with Mr. Schulte here. I hope I don't look too bad."

"You won't," he said earnestly. "You've got the machine; the rest depends on the luck of the draw."

They were lining up the lightweights now in the staging area, machines up to two hundred and fifty cubic centimeters. A few of them were junkers, but most were fairly new and well maintained. Among the heavyweights, there were a greater number of older machines but that didn't mean they were *slower* machines. I'd be lucky to survive my first pairing.

It was a great show those lightweights put on; they always *sound* faster than the heavyweights and these little speedsters were winding up.

My dad was pleased to see that the top eliminator in the class was a Temple Silver Single, a one-cylinder, two-stroke machine that was doing about 40 per cent of the business in its field in the British market.

As we lined up, in line with the right-hand lane in the staging area, Jerry asked, "Are you going to start in first?"

"Where else? I need that dig off the line."

"And go how high?" he asked.

"Not to fourth gear, certainly," I said. "I wonder what the others are doing. Man, I'm green, eh?"

Jerry grinned. "It's simple; go as high as you have to to win. Let your competition be your guide."

The lines were moving up now and I put on my helmet. In the left-hand lane ahead of us, Bud Briskin was talking to one of the Oasis City boys. This wasn't Bud's first competition, but it was his first drag. He looked less nervous than I felt.

Jerry said soothingly, "The big boys aren't here, nor the converted machines. Remember it's a sportsman's show."

I nodded.

He punched my arm. "Relax, man. You look like you're going to the gas chamber."

I took a deep breath. In a cluster of three halfway down the strip, I could see my father, Mr. Ellender and Mr. Schulte talking.

And now the pair ahead were on the line, a Triumph and a Norton, their motors revving slightly above idling, waiting for the starting light.

The light flashed, their rear wheels squealed and a smell of smoking rubber drifted back to us. The Triumph had it all the way, winning by a clean ten feet.

And on my left, my opponent looked over to grin at me. "Good omen," he said. He was mounted on a Triumph.

I smiled, revved my engine and trundled up to the line. I was all alone now; Jerry was back with the spectators.

Ahead of us, the strip stretched for more than half a mile, but only the first quarter-mile was important. It was a four-hundred-forty-yard drag.

In low, now, waiting for the light—and it flashed.

That Spitfire took off like a quarter horse and all my tension was gone. To my left, the Triumph fell back a few feet and then came even as I shifted.

He started to move by and it looked like he was going away. But he hadn't shifted; the edge was mine a split second later and I stretched it, hoping the clutch wouldn't go when I jammed into third.

The lad on the Triumph stayed with me in second; on the shift into third he gained a full two yards. The finish line wasn't more than eighty yards away and it seemed for a moment as though I was doomed to lose my first test.

And then the Spitfire seemed to tremble under the thrust of that chattering engine and we started to go by as the flag was lifted at the finish line.

It was too close for me to judge; everything was a blur as we screamed past the dropped flag and decompression fought our pace.

My opponent turned to me in wonder as we braked. I shrugged. One of us had won but neither of us knew which one.

Until the announcement came on the public address system—"Tom Manning on the BSA."

My opponent grinned as he had on the starting line. "Next time," he said jestingly, and waved.

In the pits, Jerry said, "Didn't I tell you? You'll cream 'em, all of 'em!"

My dad said, "Nice going," and Mr. Ellender nodded. I looked at Mr. Schulte.

He sighed. "You're a lost soul, now, Tom Manning. This drag business is all new to me, but I'll want to talk to you about scrambles. That's a *man's* game. That's an entirely different strategy. And so is flat-track racing."

Mr. Ellender chuckled dryly. "Welcome back, Ben, to the world you never should have left."

"Huh!" Mr. Schulte scoffed. "It's not for me. But if I can save some youngster a few bruises—" He smiled dimly. "That Triumph didn't do so well. You should get a BSA franchise, Charley."

Mr. Ellender said, "Don't you worry about Triumph, old-timer. You put on your glasses and read the record book on Triumph. And then drop over to the shop and apologize."

Mr. Schulte winked at me and said nothing.

"They're all good," my dad said. "But the Temple is going to get a lot better."

I had a hunch the air-conditioning business was about to lose one of its successful if reluctant sales engineers.

I had two more runs in my class, if I won, and I wouldn't be meeting Bud Briskin. Bud had been paired against an experienced rider on a hot machine, and been soundly trounced in his first effort.

I was up against a big single my next time out, a Royal Enfield Fury, and I didn't win it; he lost it. He was running a soft rear tire for traction; but he either didn't have a security bolt to prevent rim slippage, or it wasn't working.

The tire spun, ripping the valve, as he came screeching off the line, and it took a spectacular bit of handling on his part to keep his machine on the course until it was brought under control.

I breezed to the finish line for a hollow victory.

"One more," Jerry said when I came in. "One more and you're the winner in your class. Brother—! Onward with Crispie Crunchies."

One more. . . . I told myself that I hadn't expected to get this far; I had already achieved two victories more than I had expected. I had won the first honestly but the second had been a gift. It had been a satisfactory day.

But the meaning of "one more" was great; it would make me a winner in my class in my first competitive attempt. The tension built in me again and I rotated my shoulders, trying to work the aching stiffness out of my neck.

It was another Triumph I would be competing against; it was the man and the machine that had swamped Bud Briskin.

Watching the light, my engine revving, my right knee trembling, I kept thinking over and over again— *one more, one more, one more.* . . .

I had learned a few things in my two runs: to stay cool, to get out of first a little earlier, to run a softer rear tire. I hadn't learned enough.

The man on the Triumph must have anticipated the light. He was five feet out in front before my brain could react to the flash.

The Spitfire seemed to chatter in indignation and she almost jumped out from under me as we cut the gap to two feet before the shift.

And then, for a second, we seemed to be gaining even more and I knew we had never moved faster at this stage and hope was reborn in me.

It had a short life. With three hundred yards behind us, that Triumph lived up to its name. It began to move away steadily.

It was still going away at the finish.

In the pit, Jerry said, "I thought you had him. Something go wrong?"

"Nothing."

"That's the same guy who beat Bud," he said.

"I know."

Silence. I looked out at the staging area where they were lining up the pair for the top eliminator final.

I was gloomy. Jerry Wilson wasn't the only one who hated to lose; Tom Manning hated it, too.

My dad and Mr. Schulte came over from the refreshment stand. My dad was carrying a bottle of Coke.

He handed it to me and smiled. "Too bad. You did very well for your first day at it."

"Thanks," I said. "I sure wanted that last one."

He nodded sympathetically. Mr. Schulte said, "You did very well. That boy on the Triumph did better. Experience. There's plenty to learn in this sport; you'll be losing a lot of races."

I smiled at him. "Yes, sir. But I hope I never get to enjoy it."

Jerry laughed.

Mr. Ellender came over and said, "Tough luck, Tom. I was rooting for you." He looked coolly at Mr. Schulte. "Any remarks to make about Triumph now?"

There were no remarks. The top eliminator run was getting ready to roll, a fifty-five-inch Harley-Davidson against the Triumph that had just defeated me.

It only proved to me what a bad loser I was. Because I was rooting for the Harley, though I didn't know either contestant.

In my resentment, I had picked a winner. The Harley led all the way, a bigger machine and a rider who knew what he was doing.

On the trip home, neither Jerry nor I had much to say. Then, just as we were coming into Dune, Jerry said, "Drags are all right. But that cross-country stuff, those scrambles and Tourist Trophy runs, that's the *real* sport."

"And the dirt tracks," I added. "That's where skill counts."

"Right!" Jerry said emphatically. "Drags are for cars, for hot rods."

My father was riding in the front seat with Mr. Ellender. He turned around and smiled. "I think we're all agreed that drags aren't the real sport for one class of riders."

Neither of us said anything for a few seconds, and then Jerry asked, "What class, Mr. Manning?"

"Losers," my father said, and turned around again.

I managed a grin. I looked through the rear window to see my Spitfire bobbing along on the trailer Mr. Ellender had lent us for the day. It looked as cocky as ever, confident and ready for the rider who could give it the ride it deserved.

Jerry said quietly, "We're young, huh, Tom? We have a lot to learn."

I agreed to that though I didn't know at the time how much there was to learn. If I had, maybe I'd have gone into the air-conditioning business.

No. Those are just words. I knew what I wanted from now on. And it rode on two wheels.

Chapter 7

AUGUST WAS murder that year. For the first week we didn't have a day under a hundred and five degrees and the heat held through the nights.

I'd be entering Western Tech in September. That's on the ocean side of Los Angeles and I was almost looking forward to getting away from home. Because in freak years like this one, the desert could stay insufferable right up to Christmas.

Mr. Schulte had loaned me a pair of books to read, Jeff Smith's book on scrambling and John Surtees' book on racing. Both of these riders were immortals in their fields and both of them expressed themselves very well for nonprofessional writers. But words alone wouldn't make a rider out of me; experience in competition was what I needed.

And it was too hot to think about competition those early August days. Mr. Haskins went on vacation, which meant I had a lot of overtime hours to put in. I was glad for the extra money; I wanted to pay my dad for the cycle before school started.

The last week in August, Jerry got his cycle. It was a four-year-old Triumph and it had been used in competition. His uncle tried to point out how much work the machine needed, but Jerry was never a lad to be dismayed at the prospect of labor. And particularly when the labor was put into improving a motorcycle.

The machine had already been rebored to the maximum forty-thousandths oversize and his uncle reminded him that if the cylinder needed more boring to true it, he was in trouble.

None of his uncle's arguments prevailed. Jerry had finally found a bike he wanted at a price he could afford. He had it completely dismantled twenty-four hours after his uncle took it in trade.

Both chains were badly worn; the front-fork dampener needed replacing. The brake linings were tissue-thin. It wasn't enough to diminish Jerry's enthusiasm. He had his big machine; he had a reason for singing again.

His uncle helped him with the transmission, but the big surprise was that Mr. Schulte also came over to Mr. Ellender's shop with his own special tools. These were tools that had been stored, unused, for years, the tools that had helped him win at the Isle of Man TT, at Barcelona, at the French Grand Prix.

And then there was a third spectator at this major operation, my dad. He went over to the shop to look and listen, to get the informed word on the virtues and flaws of the machine from former TT Senior Champion, Ben Schulte.

My dad had seen another shaft drive, a Lilac, in Los Angeles and he wanted Mr. Schulte's opinion on why so few machines used it. And he wanted to talk about some of the Italian two-stroke lightweights that were coming to the front this year.

So Jerry had plenty of company evenings as he re-built that Triumph. And if a visitor from Mars had landed there he would have assumed all the transportation in America traveled on two wheels. No other kind was discussed.

That was my last pleasant memory of Dune, those nights we all worked and talked in Mr. Ellender's shop at the end of that hot August.

I was due at Western Tech for enrollment on September twenty-third; the first week in September my dad told me we were moving to the Los Angeles area.

"You're going in with Mr. Devlin?" I guessed.

He nodded.

"And how does Mom feel about it?"

He smiled. "Let's say she's only about 50 per cent as enthusiastic as I am about the change. But she is glad to get out of this heat."

Well, I suppose it sounds strange for me to say I was sad about leaving Dune. A sun-bleached little town in the middle of a million acres of sand; what could be so special about Dune?

Friends, for one. And my youth, all the days of discovery that make up an adolescence. I was moving away from the landmarks of memory.

Mr. Haskins and Mr. Schulte told me they were sorry to see me go. Mr. Haskins said, "You've been a first-rate employee from the very first day."

And Mr. Schulte said, "We'll see you again, won't we? You've got that cycle now; you'll be visiting your old friends, won't you?"

"The first weekend I'm free," I promised.

And then Jerry was pulling onto the drive atop his sweetly chugging Triumph and his grin was a little bleak.

"You're leaving us, champ," he said. "Is that right?"

I nodded.

His voice was low. "You'll come back to visit? Blood brothers, still, right?"

"Always," I said. "And you'll come to Encino to see us, won't you?"

"Natch," he said. He patted his gas tank. "On this machine, that's like running down to the corner."

All the boys were at the Dune Diner, then, and there were no funny remarks, for a change. And then home to see the moving van at the curb and I knew I was no longer a child. I was leaving that behind in Dune.

My mother looked reasonably happy as she directed the movers, but in our family we go along with decisions cheerfully, once they are definite. And though my father was leaving a firm where he was highly valued, he would never have to worry about finding a job.

As we stood on the porch, watching the van pull away, my mother said, "Let's hope it's cooler in Encino." She put a hand on my shoulder. "Blue, son?"

"In a way. But I'm looking forward to school and Dad getting into something he really enjoys. I guess you'd say I have—mixed emotions."

She smiled. "That makes two of us. Your father's certainly enthused about this new business, isn't he?"

I nodded.

"And so are you," she said.

I nodded again. "It's a very challenging field for engineers. Dad's already an engineer and I'm going to be one."

She sighed and turned to take a look around the yard. "I hope it's cooler in Encino," she said quietly.

It seemed logical to expect it would be cooler there. But Encino's in the San Fernando Valley and the Valley can get hot in September. Also, our Dune house had been air conditioned; the new one wasn't. We were a hot and tired trio when we sat down to a pickup dinner that night in our new home.

In the morning, my dad would take the freeway to the Devlin plant. That daily trip on the jammed freeway would be one aspect of the new job he wouldn't like. I had a shorter and happier trip to school, and I also had transportation that was more enjoyable.

It was a nice house, bigger than the one we'd had in Dune, and Mom could raise some flowers here. After dinner, I went out to look over the yard and then stood out in front to look at the searchlights sweeping the sky. Los Angeles is a great town for those searchlights; an Academy Award presentation or the opening of a new hamburger stand is enough excuse to wheel them out.

My dad came over to stand next to me on the front lawn. "Crazy town, isn't it?" he asked softly.

"Active town," I answered. "That's what we're looking for, isn't it, Dad—a lot of action?"

He laughed. "Maybe. At eighteen, I suppose—"
He sighed. "But I'm forty-three."

"You're a very young forty-three, Pop," I said. "And
nobody ever get's old enough to settle for what he
doesn't want, does he?"

A pause and then he gripped my shoulder. "We're
going to make it, aren't we, Tom?"

"I don't know," I said honestly. "But we're never
going to quit trying."

The next day was cooler because of an overcast, and
Mom discovered how wonderful it was to be within
walking distance of two dozen small stores and a few
big ones. The glories of Dune grew dimmer in our
memories.

At Western Tech, the emphasis is on mechanical engineering; it's one of the finest small engineering
schools in the world. Because of its concentrated
schedule, I would have quite a few hours of free time
each day. I found a job for the evenings at a filling
station two blocks from home, a mammoth eighteen-
pump operation selling an independent gas.

Practically all the attendants who worked evenings
were students, part-time workers like myself. They
were all willing to trade working hours; I would be
able to make the important meets this fall.

Dad said, "You know, you didn't *have* to take this
job. I draw a salary, too."

I joked, "But if the American Temple doesn't go
over we'll need some income."

He looked startled for a second and then saw I was

smiling. He said quietly, "That's really only half
funny." He shook his head. "At forty-three, what a
crazy decision—"

"It wouldn't have been at twenty, would it, Pop?"

"No."

"So pretend you're twenty," I told him. "You look it."

At eighteen, I could take the light view. I wondered
if I could, even at eighteen, if I had over ninety-three
thousand dollars tied up in a new venture.

Jerry came up to visit us that weekend. He had that
Triumph perking like a competition machine and it
was competition he wanted to talk about. The Ventura
Cycle Club was running a Hare Scrambles in the foothills north of their town next Sunday.

"Do you have to work?" he asked me.

"I think I can get off. Two of the men at the station
want all the Sunday work they can handle." I paused.
"Have you seen Bud Briskin lately?"

Jerry said evenly, "Not to talk with. Why?"

"I wondered how he's doing."

"He'll always do all right," Jerry said dully. "When
he isn't wheeling, he's dealing. I don't think he *ever*
sleeps."

I said no more about Bud Briskin. Evidently this was
one of Jerry's grudges he intended to maintain.

We took a ride after dinner up into the foothills
where the Burbank Scramblers used to stage their endurance runs. Some of the trails were still there,
though the signs were down and the course grown over
with gray weeds.

We still had over an hour of sunlight. It was a circus, chasing Jerry through those gullies, along those reverse camber turns, through the dried-up water splashes and over what was left of the jumps. He'd called it right at Oasis City; *this* was the true cycle sport.

We came over the last rise the fourth time around and I shifted quickly into third and twisted the throttle. Jerry had shifted earlier; he had a twenty-foot lead as we came down that straightaway run to the former finish line.

My Spitfire seemed to fly. A third of the way through the stretch I was closing the gap fast and Jerry looked around to see me coming up. He made a mistake in strategy then.

He went into high gear, though there was less than two hundred yards of course left and he must have realized there was no room for the potential of his high gear.

I went past him as he shifted; I was still gaining on him as the Spitfire soared across the finish line.

I slowed and waited and he called, "Come on—once more around."

"It's getting dark," I said. "Too many rocks in there to take a chance in the dark."

"Come on!" he urged. "You didn't really beat me. Give me a chance to get even."

I kept my face blank. "Beat you—? Were we racing?"

He stared at me, perplexed and partially belligerent. And then when he saw I was hamming it, he chuckled. "All right. We weren't racing. But next Sunday we will be."

"Right," I said. "You'd better be ready."

He trundled his cycle over next to mine and we looked back on the dust from our exertions, still floating in the air.

He asked, "Why did you let me lead all the way until the end?"

"I didn't know the course, Jerry. I figured if there were any stray rocks on the trail, you might as well hit 'em first."

He chuckled again. "I keep thinking *I'm* the only competitive one. That's bad thinking—it could lose me some races."

I didn't say anything. To me, losing races was to be expected. And watching Jerry's technique as I had followed him around that deserted course, I knew he was going to lose a lot of races. It was all throttle to Jerry; successful scrambling depended on *strategy*, too.

He left for home Sunday noon from the station. I had arranged to work from noon to midnight so I could be off the following Sunday. I was scheduled for a busy week.

But I still found time two evenings during that week to run over to that course we had used and put the Spitfire through her paces. I practiced on the jump, learning to land with the rear wheel low and digging. There was a grass stretch where I learned what that kind of surface can do to traction.

I also learned I would need better shoes than the ones I was wearing. On the tight turns, a rider has to drag the inward foot for stability and that takes stout leather. On the short, flat tracks, only the left foot is dragged and an iron can be worn for that; but scrambles have both right and left turns and some of them are tricky hairpins.

Saturday night, my dad said, "I'm going with you tomorrow. We can slide that cycle into the station wagon, can't we?"

"Easily," I said. "Are you going to be my pit crew?"

I was joking, but he said seriously, "Only an observer. Ben Schulte's going to be your pit crew."

"Ben Schulte—?"

He nodded. "I've seen him twice this week. He's a sort of—competitive consultant for the American Temple." He opened his brief case and took out a piece of drawing paper. "What do you think of this?"

It was the old and honored Temple insignia except that it was now imposed on a background. The background was a line drawing of the United States boundaries, and in small script above the larger "Temple" was the word "American."

"Refined and elegant," I said. "Is that all that's going to be changed?"

He smiled. "So far, the changes have been minor. But Walter and Ben are dreaming up some wild ones. I've had to represent the conservative view." He paused. "I'm glad I made the move, though. It is a real challenge, this job."

My challenge would come tomorrow, up at Ventura. Somehow, I didn't consider the drag a test; there wasn't too much skill involved in a straightaway acceleration run. A drag was more a test of the machine than of the rider. A scrambles race didn't always go to the fastest machine. It was a test of traction, calculated risk and patience, motorcycling at its sporting best.

I worked at the station until ten-thirty that night and got to bed about eleven. I was nervous about tomorrow but luckily it had been a busy day. I fell asleep immediately.

In the morning, at breakfast, my dad asked me, "Remember Johnny Burke, the rider Mr Ellender introduced us to at the Sagebrush Scrambles?"

"Of course," I said. "He's one of my heroes, Pop."

"He might be working for us next year," my father said.

"You mean you'll have some competition models ready by next year?"

He nodded. "And Johnny Burke wants to ride them. He also wants to put some money into the firm."

I said nothing.

My father said, "Why so sad? You look disappointed about something."

I took a breath. "Do I? I guess—maybe I thought I'd be riding for Temple, when the time came."

"You will," he said blithely. "But as an Amateur. You won't be an Expert for a couple years. Johnny's an Expert now." He smiled. "He'll be at Ventura today. You can test yourself against him."

Chapter 8

THE VENTURA CYCLE CLUB had strict membership rules and maintained them rigidly. It was a *club,* not a *gang,* and all its members were agreed that motorcycling was a gentleman's sport. They ran their meets with that thought in mind.

All the officials were neatly dressed; all wore identifying caps and name badges. Both the spectators' and the participants' cars were restricted to the immense parking lot; all one saw in the barricaded pit area were motorcycles.

Mr. Schulte was waiting for us near the refreshment stand in the center of the pit area. It was good to see him again. He helped us unload the Spitfire and he was checking it over two minutes later in the pit assigned to us.

Not far from us, Bud Briskin was bent over his Tornado; I went over there.

"Stranger!" he said. "Is it true your dad's working for Temple now?"

"In a way. Mr. Devlin made a deal with the Temple people to put out an American machine. And Temple's getting the same deal for one of the Devlin scooters." I tried to look modest. "So my dad went into the new concern as executive vice-president."

Bud's eyes were wide. "And you'll be getting a new machine every year, right?"

"Nothing like that," I said.

"Sure you will. And that Spitfire will be for sale. You let me know when it is, Tom."

"All right. If it is, I'll let you know." I paused. "Why don't you drive up to Encino and visit us once in a while?"

He smiled wryly. "I planned to do that last week. And then I heard Jerry was going, so—" He shrugged. "Is he making this meet?"

"He told me he was. He's still not talking to you?"

Bud sighed. "That's right. And in a town the size of Dune, that's not easy. Kid stuff—I wish he'd grow up."

A few machines away, Johnny Burke was tinkering with his Triumph. Beyond him, I saw Red Dunn and Ed Garvey. I said, "Jerry had better grow up. He's playing with the big boys, now."

Bud grinned. "Aren't we all?"

When I got back to our pit, Mr. Ellender and Jerry were there.

"Nervous?" Jerry asked me.

"About the same as you," I admitted. "A lot of talent here."

He nodded quietly, his eyes roaming over the immense pit area.

I said, "Why don't you go over and say 'hello' to Bud Briskin?"

He shook his head, staring out at what we could see

of the course; the winding uphill trail, the water hole fifty yards beyond the biggest jump, the gullies hidden from our view.

"It looks rugged," he said.

"Seven miles of test," I said. "Grass, mud, water. Uphill, downhill, reverse turns, jumps and tricky gravel. I wonder how many will finish?"

"I will," he said, "if I have to carry the machine."

Then Mr. Schulte said, "How about that mixture, Tom? Hasn't it seemed lean to you?"

"A little," I admitted. "She seemed to starve out under heavy load, Mr. Schulte."

"Call me Ben," he said. "You're a big boy now."

That made it official.

My father came over to stand next to me. "Easy does it, Tom. You're here to learn, so you can be worth something to us next year. On the first trip around, just stroll. Keep your eyes open and your competitive spirit dormant. Am I coming through?"

"Strong and clear," I said. "Having fun, Pop?"

He smiled. "I've just turned twenty-one. I can vote now."

Mr. Ellender said, "I only feel about sixty-eight, myself, about Ben's age. I suppose Johnny Burke on that Triumph is a cinch to win, isn't he?"

"He'll have to beat me," Jerry said, and looked surprised because we laughed.

When my dad had told me to *stroll* on my first trip around the course he wasn't speaking literally, of course. What he had meant was that I should drive

well below the maximum effort in order to learn the
dangers and opportunities of the layout. There would
undoubtedly be stretches where near-top speed could
be reached; there would be turns and areas of minimum traction where the machine would be scarcely
moving.

Everybody entered would be going into it blind,
though it was undoubtedly similar to other courses
previously laid out here. But one new unexpected turn
could change a lot of destinies.

The racket was growing now as the crowd grew,
and as rider after rider throttled his engine, listening
to the bark, trying to find the pitch that meant it was
perfectly tuned.

The heavyweights would start first, and the assistant
starter came over to get us assigned to our starting
position. Ben came along.

Two bikes away, Ed Garvey sat on his Norton, ad-
justing his helmet webbing.

Ben said, "If you can do it, and it will take some doing, try to keep Ed in sight. He has a reputation for
slow starts and fast finishes. Tail him, if you can.
Watch his route on corners, trust his speed on grass.
You can get an education, tailing a man like Ed Garvey."

"I'll try," I said. "But if he starts at a speed too fast
for me, I'm not going to take the chance. I figure I'll
be lucky to stay upright and in one piece."

Ben nodded. "You're right. I keep forgetting how
new you are to this." He sighed, and patted my shoulder. "Luck, boy. I'll keep you informed."

Two cycles beyond Ed, Johnny Burke was set and ready, his eyes on the starter's flag. Ben went away and I had never felt more like a boy in a man's world.

So what did I have to prove? Ninety-nine per cent of the riders had more experience than I had. I was here to learn, not to win. I was here to make myself capable of winning later.

These things I tried to tell myself as I waited for the starter's flag to drop. But who enters any contest with no thought of winning? Who lives without dreams? Who wants to?

Under me, the Spitfire chattered sharply, ready for any challenge, equal to any summons. All along the line, the eyes were on the flag, the engine racket seeming to grow as we waited.

The flag dropped.

It was like a combination artillery bombardment and cavalry charge as sixty detonating heavyweights rocketed for position into the wide, sweeping, uphill trail that led toward the hills.

It wasn't hard for me to keep Ed Garvey in sight through this first half-mile of jockeying. He was doing his own trailing; dropping in behind Red Dunn's climbing Norton, letting Red set the pace for *him*.

The course was wide here, the traction firm. I kept the Spitfire in third gear, ignoring the eager beavers who were passing me on both sides, watching Ed who was watching Red. Almost at the plateau above, I could see Johnny Burke's Triumph leading the field. Johnny played this game differently from Ed, but Johnny was a champion and had earned the right to his own strategy.

A fairly tight left turn, now, with adverse camber, and I watched Ed carefully. On tricky going like this, too much speed can spin you end for end; not enough and you lose the rear wheel down the bank.

I watched the way Ed leaned, I tried to exactly match his speed without losing my own sense of safe traction. Directly ahead, a Temple twin started to slide and her rider accelerated savagely.

The rear wheel came around, the front came up— and both man and machine went sliding backward down the bank, out of the action.

The plateau, a curving trail—and mud.

I saw Red's Norton scoot for the extreme edge of the mudhole and realized the strategy there. The middle of it just had to be muddier and deeper. Garvey chose the other edge; I was too close now to see who had picked the safest route.

I followed Ed's choice. I tried to match his pace. He was staying in third. At any rate, he didn't shift.

Mud splashed, the Spitfire coughed and my new boots no longer looked new. But there was no wobble in my mount; we plowed through steadily, with dry ignition, once more onto firmer ground and almost a mile ahead in clear view.

It was slightly uphill but perfectly tractionable surface and a straight run. We went into high gear, my eyes on Ed's back.

He flew. My heart hammered and the Spitfire

shrieked and I was forced to give most of my atten·· tion to the road, but we trailed him at a pace I would never have attempted alone. I couldn't see Red Dunn and wondered if we had left him behind in the mudhole.

To our right an enormous sign proclaimed: *Calamity Rock ahead. Top of course.*

I had heard about that, about the S-turn that wound around the near side of the rock and the water splash a hundred yards beyond it.

I could see Ed shifting down; at the same spot I followed his example. Ahead of Ed, I saw a Triumph ride into the first left turn much too fast and go tilting down the bank off the course. I could see now why a sturdy leather suit was a must for *this* sport.

Ed took the left turn wide, sweeping cleanly into the following right turn that hugged the wall of the red rock towering above us. The trail was narrow here and the drop-off steep; I forgot Ed for a moment and concentrated on the preservation of Tom Manning, novice punk.

Gravel now, the rock behind us, blocking off a view of our pursuers. Into high, but not barreling, watching for the water splash to come.

Plain enough to see and looking shallow. I stayed in high because Ed did but wondered why he cut his speed so sharply. I had an urge to maintain the pace but remembered Ben Schulte's advice. I cut my pace to match Ed's.

It was a shallow splash and absolutely no threat to a protected ignition. *I could have kept my pace,* I thought, *I should have. . . .*

And then I saw the grass beyond the water and realized what traction wet tires would have afforded me *there*. Though the curve that followed was not tight, it would have been far too tight for wet tires on dormant grass.

I breathed a small prayer of thankfulness as we slid around the turn, as I saw Ned Phillips to one side, trying to kick his Gold Star into life. Ned must have gone down and killed his engine.

Straight course now but downhill and on grass. I let Ed gain on me again. He knew this kind of surface and I didn't, not from two short evenings during the week.

And then we were on flat going, on gravel, and the Spitfire chattered her impatience, and I stretched a little the calculation of my calculated risk.

I didn't gain on Ed. I hadn't expected to. He gained only a few yards on me, a moral victory for Tom Manning. And then, far ahead of Ed, I saw a rider and cycle outlined against the overcast sky and thought it had to be a mirage.

A jump—? After a downhill run, a jump? I could wind up in orbit. I watched Ed, trying to gauge his pace, as we sped closer to the mirage.

On my right, a comet went by, a young lad on a big Harley, heading for disaster. Hadn't he seen that rider in the air?

What had Jeff Smith written about jumps? The front wheel about eighteen inches higher than the rear on landing, I remember that. And a thrust of power, just as the front wheel started on its air travel. And don't try to jump high; no rear wheel can find traction in the atmosphere.

That had been written by an expert, but I wasn't an expert and races are not run in books. This was for real and I didn't feel prepared.

Ahead, the wild kid on the Harley had shot past Ed Garvey, but Ed maintained his pace, oblivious to the implied challenge. Ed had seen a lot of wild kids in his time, but never in the winner's circle.

Okay, old-timer, I thought. *Lead me home. Lead me safely past this jump; I'm here to learn.*

Ahead of him I could see the jump now. There was about fifty yards of flat course that looked tractionable between the bottom of the hill and the ramp before the jump. I watched to see if Ed would shift down here.

I could hear by his bark that he was easing off on the throttle, but it was clear he didn't intend to shift. Even at half-throttle, he had plenty of speed to coast over the fifty yards of flat and up the ramp.

From where I rode, I couldn't see his throttle hand; but I listened to the bark of the Norton, trying to determine when a twist of his wrist would give him the impetus to jump well and low.

I wasn't riding the same machine; I would have to adjust his strategy to my machine, hoping I had figured it right.

He was on the flat now, through it, climbing the ramp—and I listened. He must have read Jeff Smith's book, too; the power came on just as his front wheel left the ground.

Okay, Tom Manning, here goes nothing. . . .

The Spitfire was confident, but I wasn't. I forced all thought of disaster from my mind and tried to play it cool, cool and calculating, like a minor-league Ed Garvey.

Onto the flat and up the ramp—and *now!*

A twist of the wrist as the front wheel cleared the edge and we were soaring. Without wings or propellers or even small jet engines, the Spitfire took to the air, front wheel high, rear low and all the hundreds of spectators looking like ants, two miles away and far below us.

Was I scared? Yes. Was it a thrill? You'd have to try it. It was flying without wings; what greater thrill can there be? Ask any ski jumper.

I say without modesty I landed well and put her on full throttle the instant we were back to earth. In a tangle of brush to my right, the lad who had passed me on the Harley stared at me vacantly as I thundered on. He was standing, but his bike wasn't and the bend in his front fork made it clear he was through for the day.

Full throttle, a fine surface, the Spitfire giving her all, and still I didn't gain on Ed. And a glance behind showed me that another star was coming up; big Red Dunn on his big Norton.

A sweeping, wide turn ahead and gravel. I studied Ed's technique and forgot Red, coming up from behind. I wanted to see Ed's line through the turn.

He went into it fast and sharp and, though I was fifty

feet behind him, gravel rattled off my goggles and I was glad they were shatterproof.

He was swinging now, sending a fantail of gravel onto the spectators behind the hay bales here. He was under acceleration, maintaining his control by the thrust of his rear wheel, handling the turn like the old pro he was.

I had slowed, hoping to use the same power drive through the corner without the need of dragging a foot.

I was low and leaning when the rear wheel started to slide. Automatically, my left foot dropped to the gravel, but the drag of it swung me even wider and for a frightening fraction of a second, I was out of control and ready to leave the machine.

In that wild second, Red Dunn made his move.

He came through on the inside of me, the gravel-free side, and was out of the bend and gaining on Ed before I could bring the sliding Spitfire under control.

I didn't chase him. He had shown me the difference between a man and a boy through that treacherous gravel; his superiority was firmly established in my mind. His *present* superiority, I added to myself grimly.

I was here to learn, not to win, I reminded myself again. Ahead, Red was crowding Ed Garvey as we came into the straight, smooth going that led to the finish of the first lap. The spectators were lined two deep along a quarter of a mile here, all eyes on the Garvey-Dunn duel.

My own eyes were on the pits to the left, searching for the red-and-yellow-checked jacket that would identify Ben Schulte for me.

He had no instructions, only a raised right hand with the thumb and forefinger forming an "O," his signal to me that I was doing as well as we had a right to expect.

A comforting signal from a T T Senior Champion and I should have been happier than I was. But underneath the discipline I was trying to develop I smarted at the easy way Red Dunn had handled me on that curve.

Climbing again on the wide slope, and I stole a quick glance behind to see what the competition there was doing. There were four cycles within two hundred yards, only one within reasonable challenging distance at the moment.

I couldn't be sure, but it looked like Bud Briskin. Ahead, Dunn had moved past Garvey and both of them were almost to the rim of the plateau. Both of them were now moving at a speed I couldn't hope to match.

The left turn with adverse camber again, a wider right turn and the curving trail that ended at the plateau and the mud splash. It was shallower now, spread and partly dried by the wheels of all the cycles that had crossed it.

Through it faster than the first trip, up the gradual incline at full throttle toward Calamity Rock. Around the S-curve, crowding the rock, keeping my eyes averted from the cliff to the left of this narrow trail.

That second trip around was easier on my mind even without Ed Garvey as a guide. I passed two bikes that were still moving and two that weren't and came down to a repetition of the same signal I had received on my first lap—the "O" that meant I was riding up to present expectations.

He added a signal this time, spreading his hands, palms inward, about half the distance the length of his arms would permit. That meant the closest competitor behind me was fifty yards back. I wondered who it was.

Though I no longer had Garvey as a pilot, I had the remembrance of his sound technique and I had the knowledge of how my bike differed from his. That third round, I knew, was faster than the other two had been and Ben's signal this trip was a new one—one clenched fist aloft. He meant I was now riding better than I had a right to expect, using the rough translation.

He hadn't given me a signal about my closest competition. At least I didn't see it. But I saw the competition about ten seconds later.

I had been right, two laps ago; it was Bud Briskin. He moved up to my right on the slope, his Tornado chopping them off sweetly. He glanced over and grinned, a challenging grin. I nodded and increased my pace slightly, awaiting a reaction from him.

It came. His machine moved out, his rear wheel spurting dust, and he was bent low and logging as I trailed him on the dust-free side. I had no immediate plans to pass him; he obviously had been traveling at the same speed I had and was now traveling faster.

He would be my new Ed Garvey, my pilot ship, leading me to the harbor of the checkered flag.

I won't bore you with all the details of that chase. This Briskin boy was better than Tom Manning at our present stage of development. It didn't give him the complete edge, though. My machine was designed for scrambles and it had been tuned by Ben Schulte. What I lacked in skill was made up in machine; Bud didn't run away from me.

But what a pace he set for us!

I let him have twenty yards and never let it grow beyond fifty, making no effort to challenge. We passed some laggards in those screaming rounds but we had no way of knowing if they were in the same lap. Some of them were lightweights and that was a separate race.

And then, as we rocketed past the yellow flag that told us we were heading into our last lap, delusions of glory took over the mind of Tom Manning.

I had a better machine and only a little less skill than Bud Briskin; why should I finish behind him? I decided to make my move.

Trailing him, I had studied him and noticed that when he covered the pair of reverse turns before the mudhole, he made the first of these turns wide. He probably did this to get a better line into the second turn, but it seemed to me he didn't need that much of an arc.

Going up the wide slope, I followed him closely, shifting into third about twenty feet short of the first turn. He went wide—and I charged.

The Spitfire jumped, her rear tire squealing, and shot for a line to the left of Bud's sweeping right turn. My left foot scraped the hay bale as I cut back sharply into the second turn, as Bud crowded me from the right.

I had no place to go but forward and that was the path I took at full throttle, Bud to my right and losing no ground.

Both of us were at full speed up the gradual incline now, at full speed and heading for the mudhole.

I stole a glance to my right; it was clear that Bud was determined to get past, even if it meant full gun into the sticky going ahead.

Well, I had as much traction as he did and almost as much skill; if we went down, we would go down together.

It was no problem so far as traction was concerned. The mud had been scattered by all those churning wheels; the hole was almost dry. It was more jump than mudhole now. We came out of it with our front wheels in the air but our rear wheels still driving.

We went up the long fast stretch toward Calamity Rock at a speed beyond any I had traveled today and I felt no fear, my confidence growing perhaps too quickly. But I didn't want Bud to have the lead when we came to that narrow trail at the top of the course.

And then ahead I saw Jerry for the first time during

that run. He was leaning into the first of the reverse
curves as we both bore down on his wildly sliding Triumph.

We were almost on him by the time he came into the
second turn and a three-bike tangle was shaping up.
Both Bud and I slowed, eating Jerry's dust, as our impatient machines barked at the delay.

Coming into the narrow trail that threaded the edge
of the rock on one side and the cliff on the other I managed to cut in behind Jerry and ahead of Bud.

And then, as we funneled out onto the broader trail,
both Bud and I pulled even, Bud on the right of Jerry,
I on the left.

And that's the way we hit the water hole, three
abreast.

It had been refilled; it was like smashing a tidal
wave. Bud took the extreme right edge, I the extreme
left edge. And where did that leave Jerry? You
guessed it.

He must have thought he had missed the trail
and run into Niagara Falls. Over the sounds of two
other engines, I could hear the Triumph sputter, backfire and then regain its tempo as the heat of the engine dried out the splashed ignition.

But that misfire had been enough to put Jerry well
behind as Bud and I fought a precarious duel for dominance on the grassy downslope that followed.

I led into the flat that followed the grass; Bud was
not in sight at either side of me as we started the
downhill run. I didn't look back to see how strong

was my lead. There was a jump coming up at the end of this slope and I knew I was going into it at the fastest speed I had traveled today.

The jump alone didn't disturb me, but jumping with another rider only a few feet behind was an experience new to me and my imagination made the most of it.

Then the thought came to me that it might be a new experience for Bud, too, jumping so close to another rider. Bud was behind; the choice would be his.

The bottom of the slope, the short flat run to the ramp, up the ramp—and sailing. I had tried to stay low but my speed had been too great; I went out and up.

I couldn't have been air-borne more than a second or two, but a number of thoughts flashed through my thick head. And the important one was regret at my stupidity. If I intended to travel at a speed beyond my present skill, it had been stupid to risk it three-quarters of the way through my *last* lap. I couldn't have picked a dumber time to crash.

So, all right, Tom Manning, *don't crash*. Keep your front wheel up, your rear wheel ready to drive. Think about nothing beyond the job at hand, one second at a time.

The rear wheel grounded first, with a jolt that rattled my teeth and I waited for the "bang" of a tire. It didn't come; we went charging along the flat, well-surfaced stretch that fed into the big gravel curve.

There was still no sign of Bud on either side of me.

I thought about the gravel curve half a mile ahead, remembering how Ed Garvey had spanned it, remembering how Red Dunn had taken me there.

I had my own line through this curve by now and I intended to follow it despite any move Bud might make.

I never saw him until we were out of the turn. He had taken a line that brought him inside me into the stretch to the finish, a line smarter than mine had been. Because he was gaining as we hit the straight smooth going toward the raised checkered flag.

Ben Schulte was the winner in that spurt; he had tuned the Spitfire to her top potential and both bikes were wide open now. Slowly, as the faces of the spectators on both sides went past in a blur, Bud dropped back, back, back. . . .

I finished twenty feet ahead of him, going away.

A hundred yards past the finish line, we both turned off and I waited for him.

He was grinning. He idled over and said simply, "Next time."

"Don't be a good loser," I said. "It makes me uncomfortable. I wonder how we finished."

He shrugged.

And then, as we chugged slowly back to the pits, he said, "That bath we gave Jerry Wilson—that was the unkindest cut of all. He'll have *two* men to hate now."

I chuckled. "No. Jerry knows it's all in the game. You pass where you can in this kind of race."

Then Ben Schulte and my dad were coming over to

congratulate us, and my dad said, "You finished eighth, Tom. That's wonderful!"

"Better than ninth," Bud said. "Was Jerry tenth?"

"He just went by," my dad said. "He still has a lap to go."

"Ouch!" Bud said. "Tom, we not only gave him a bath; we lapped him. Who won?"

"Red Dunn," Ben said. "Johnny Burke was second, Garvey third." He put a hand on my shoulder. "Our boy was the first Novice to finish."

"Congratulations," Bud said. "I'll know who to watch from now on."

We were still standing there, joking and laughing, when Jerry came in.

We saw him when he was about fifty feet away, heading toward us, and I should have realized it was no time to laugh.

But he had had a full circuit and more of that dusty trail since we had soaked him at the water splash. And we had soaked him well. His wet body had been a magnet for all the dust he had traveled through since. He was caked; he looked like a moving statue.

I started to laugh and Bud joined in. We couldn't help it.

For about two seconds Jerry stared at us and then he deserted his bike and came charging over, heading for Bud.

Bud stopped laughing and waited quietly—as I went over to stop Jerry.

Chapter 9

"GET OUT of my way," he said. "I'll fight you both, but Bud first. Get out of my way."

"Grow up," I said. "You're playing with the men now, Jerry, and it's time to come of age."

"Get out of my way or start swinging," he said. "I was a lap behind you two—you didn't have to pass me there."

Mr. Ellender said, "Jerry, calm down. Right now!"

He made no sign that he had heard. He was glaring at me. "You two thought it was very funny, didn't you? You could have put me out of the race."

"We didn't," I said. "Better riders than you have been splashed out of races. You were lucky."

He took a step toward me, his right fist clenched— and Mr. Ellender stepped in quickly to hold him by the shoulders as Ben came over to help.

Mr. Ellender said quietly, "Apologize, Jerry. You owe both the boys an apology."

"Never!" he said. He twisted away from his uncle and walked over toward their car, ignoring all of us.

Mr. Ellender sighed and said, "Well, gentlemen, I apologize for him. He'll—come around." He went over to get Jerry's bike and follow him toward the parking lot.

My dad asked, "What happened?"

I told him.

He smiled. "Jerry has a lot to learn. I hope he does. Because he's a good boy."

Ben Schulte said, "He'll learn. More painfully than most of us, but don't ever doubt that he'll learn. He's a stubborn boy and a little spoiled, but he's not dumb. He'll *have* to learn."

I agreed with that.

Bud said jestingly, "And I'll learn, too. I'll learn to beat Tom Manning. I thought I had you, after that turn."

"The machine beat you," I said. "Not I."

My father said, "Bud, we've a new carburetor for that model I'd like to see tested in competition. You would be doing me a favor by accepting one free."

Bud grinned. "Why not? If you can't lick 'em, join 'em. Thank you, Mr. Manning. Tom has my address."

Eighth place. . . . It doesn't sound like much but I was happy with it. Only Jerry's unreasonable temper kept it from being a completely satisfactory day.

We loaded the Spitfire back into the wagon and I climbed into the front seat while my father lingered to arrange some meeting with Ben Schulte. I tried to tell myself that Jerry's childish fireworks had no meaning, that he'd be back to normal tomorrow, and ashamed of his display.

But his dislike of Bud Briskin had stayed constant for months, now, and there had been no excuse for it. As kids, we had fought often. Though I was bigger and stronger, Jerry had never considered that when his temper boiled.

We were no longer children. We were active participants in an exciting but dangerous game. In the heat of competition a man with a grudge was courting trouble and inviting disaster in this precarious sport. I didn't want that man to be Jerry Wilson.

My dad climbed in behind the wheel and started the engine. "You look gloomy," he commented. "You rode a beautiful race, son."

"Thank you," I said. "I was thinking of Jerry."

My father sighed. "He'll get over it." A pause. "Don't you think so? You know him better than I do." He turned out onto the highway.

I said, "He was always competitive. But lately—" I shrugged.

My dad said, "You two have been good friends. If that ends, I'm sure it won't be your fault, Tom. But you can't spend all your life worrying about Jerry Wilson. He's old enough now to learn some self-discipline, and you'll have other boys to worry about, *champions.* I repeat, you did very well today. Ben Schulte thinks you're a natural."

I gulped, saying nothing.

My father chuckled. "And compliments from Ben Schulte don't come every day."

"That's for sure," I said, and we laughed, heading for home, and the importance of Jerry's anger was diminished in my mind.

For two months I was too busy to get any more

competitive experience. My studies and the work at the station took up all the hours I wasn't sleeping or eating. In those two months, there was a track race at Palm Vista and about half a dozen scrambles or cross-country races in our end of the state.

Bud Briskin came up to see me. Bud had taken two fourths at Palm Vista and finished third in a hill climb up at Santa Barbara. He told me he would be enrolling at Western Tech in February.

Bud had started earning his own living at the age of fourteen, and he knew how limited a man without a college degree was in today's world.

"And I certainly don't intend to race motorcycles the rest of my life," he said. "Do you?"

"Not for a living," I agreed. "But it's a great sport." I paused. "And if I get good enough at it, I'll be racing for a living in an indirect way."

"Indirect—?" He frowned. "Oh, you mean if you're riding a Temple?"

"That's it. Dad and Mr. Devlin agree that there's no better advertising than a few wins at big meets."

Bud grinned. "A few *wins*—? Nothing personal, but are you ready to deliver those?"

"Not yet. That's why they're hiring Johnny Burke for next year."

"But you'll be riding a Temple?"

I shrugged. "I hope."

"And the Spitfire will be for sale," Bud went on. "And I already have a customer for *my* Temple."

I laughed. "Man, you *always* have a customer waiting, don't you?"

My dad had sent the new carburetor to Bud and Bud had promptly sent back a full report on how it had improved the performance of his machine. He still didn't feel that it was up to my Spitfire, but as I explained to him, that Spitfire had been tuned by an expert.

I didn't ask him about Jerry and Jerry didn't write or come to visit. Perhaps, I thought, he feels embarrassed. So I wrote to him.

He didn't answer.

In March, there was to be another meet at Palm Vista and it looked as though I'd be able to make it. That meant I would have to remove the brake shoes and operating cams from both wheels of the Spitfire, because all dirt track and speedway motorcycle racing is run without brakes. Ben Schulte came up the weekend before the race to help me with the job.

Without the brakes, I couldn't ride the cycle to school the following week; I drove Mom's car. It was like driving a truck, though it was a small and adequately powered car. It was a mystery to me why people who traveled alone thought they needed four wheels.

At school, Bud told me he would be making the Palm Vista meet. And, he had heard from the Dune Diner, so would Jerry.

"Have you seen him lately?" he asked.

I shook my head. "I wrote to him. He didn't answer."

Bud smiled grimly. "I hear he's worked a few more

horses into that Triumph." A pause. "You two are good friends; you've been friends for ten years. Do you think he didn't write because he's embarrassed?"

"Maybe. But Jerry's always been a bad loser. He admits it."

Bud sniffed. "These people who freely admit their faults—and then don't do a thing about correcting them *give me a pain.* Well, he'd better not get lippy around me—"

Bud was no taller than Jerry, but he was a lot huskier; I, too, hoped that Jerry wouldn't get lippy. Bud had said we'd been friends for ten years; he had understated it. We had been best friends for almost fifteen years.

And one water splash could end that?

Not quite. The soaking had only been one incident. Being lapped by his contemporaries, one of whom rode the cycle Jerry wanted, had added significance to the splashing. And Jerry operated on the bullheaded principle that his enemies should be his friends' enemies. My friendship with Bud Briskin galled him.

None of the nationally known riders would be at Palm Vista, but there would be two competitors there determined to give me a race, Bud and Jerry.

I would need both leather pants and jacket for this kind of racing, and a steel shoe for my left foot. I had saved enough to buy my own, but Dad decided American Temple should foot the bill.

"We'll call it an investment in your potential," he said. "Ben thinks you're a comer."

"I think Bud *is*," I said, "and Sunday he'll have the new carburetor. And Jerry has been working on his machine."

He smiled. "Don't concentrate on them. There'll be other riders at Palm Vista with much more experience." He looked at me soberly. "Never make a race *personal*. Do you know what I mean by that?"

I nodded. I asked, "Were you thinking of Jerry Wilson?"

"Not particularly." He put a hand on my shoulder. "I was thinking of you. *You're* my problem. I guess you know your mother isn't comfortable about this racing."

"I'll be careful," I said. "I'll never take any unnecessary chances."

He smiled sadly. "I know that. It's the *necessary* chances you'll be taking that worry me."

He was right; there were plenty of those. On a mile track, most of the machines would be doing around a hundred miles an hour on the straightaways and about seventy in a controlled slide on the turns. A controlled slide at seventy miles an hour could so easily turn into an *uncontrolled* slide.

No brakes were allowed, and once a rider reached high gear he was not permitted to change to any of the lower gears in a race. This was a new technique for me after scrambles and drags; I hoped I wouldn't diminish Ben Schulte's opinion of my potential.

We left for Palm Vista early Sunday morning. It was only a two-hour drive, but I would need to do a few circuits of the track for practice under the professional eyes of Ben Schulte.

On a straightaway run in track racing, the rider slides back to a pillion on top of the rear fender and lays his chest along the top of the gas tank for minimum wind resistance. I had never ridden that way, nor learned to slide around a turn at a speed anywhere near seventy miles an hour.

I tried to remember all I had read in John Surtees' book, but it would be Ben who would judge how well I had digested what I had read.

It was eight o'clock when we turned into the entrants' road at Palm Vista, the road that carried us through a tunnel under the track and into the infield behind the pits.

There were only two other cycles in view, both carrying green plates with white numbers, identifying the riders as Novices. My plate would be red with white numbers—a Probationary Novice. The Experts had white plates, the Amateurs yellow, both with black numbers. There would be no Experts here today, but it seemed likely there would be some respected Amateurs.

We were unloading the cycle when Ben Schulte arrived. He and my dad went over to the judges' stand as soon as we were unloaded; I stayed with the machine, waiting to learn what pit we had been assigned.

I was checking the tires when I saw Mr. Ellender's Pontiac come into the infield, towing the trailer that held Jerry's Triumph.

I bent over the Spitfire as the Pontiac headed my way. The first word would have to be Jerry's; it was his move.

The Pontiac continued toward the other end of the pits. I straightened again, feeling a tinge of regret and a strange loneliness. Jerry must have seen me.

I slipped the steel protector on my left shoe and adjusted the webbing in my helmet. Dad and Ben came back and we trundled the bike over to our pit.

Dad asked, "Wasn't that Charley Ellender's Pontiac that pulled in a few minutes ago?"

I nodded.

He said, "I think I'll run over and talk with Charley. You boys won't need me here." He left us.

Ben Schulte sighed and said nothing.

I said, "Jerry will come around. He's a stubborn boy."

"I know," Ben said. "I know the type exactly." He paused. "I was a stubborn boy, too. It cost me some good friends and some big races." He seemed to shake himself. "All right, now, young man, this is all new to you and—"

And he talked while I listened. He talked about the speed groove and the way it would pack through the laps and how rough the track would become outside of the groove and through the turns. I would have to leave the groove to pass; he wanted me to be prepared for the shocking change in surface and traction.

He said, "You're a pretty sensible lad. You know

your limits, I hope. Don't *ever* ride beyond what you know to be your personal limit, no matter how tempted you might be in competition. You're here to learn. *Remember that!*"

I nodded, smiling at the earnestness of his tone.

"Don't grin at me," he said. "It's a crazy sport you're in."

"*We're* in, Ben," I said. "And you love it."

"Okay, okay." He rubbed the back of his neck and frowned at the sun. "It's going to be a dusty day. Crazy country—hot weather in March."

"Cycle country," I said. "Should I try a few laps?"

"A few *slow* laps," he said.

A few slow laps. . . . A freshly groomed track, a perfectly tuned Spitfire and a bright new morning. I may have been a sensible lad, as Ben had stated, but I was also human. I took one slow lap and then tried another at about twenty more miles per hour.

No strain, no wobble, not a second of lost traction. I bent low and twisted the throttle.

We were really barreling past the deserted grandstand, past the dozen or so watching occupants of the pits, past the refreshment stand and into the south turn.

My judgment of pace had been sadly wrong; I should have listened more carefully to Ben. Because suddenly the outside fence on that turn seemed to be coming directly at me.

The steel-shod foot went down as I swung to the left, showering the fence with dirt, the rear wheel trying to get out in front where it decidedly didn't belong.

My heart went up as my foot went down, up to my throat, where it stuck. For a moment, the planet seemed to teeter on the edge of lost orbit; I was out of control and still sliding toward the fence.

And then I realized only a thrust of power would save me and it took all my will to speed a machine that was already moving too fast. I twisted the grip—and we were back in business.

No brakes, I told myself shakily. *Remember that, Tom Manning. This is another technique and you had better learn it fast.* I finished the lap under half-steam.

In our pit, Ben glared at me.

"I know," I said. "You warned me. I apologize."

He shook his head. "That was a Jerry Wilson display."

"Guilty. Ben, you've done a beautiful job on that machine."

"Don't soap me," he said gruffly. "Listen; don't talk."

From down the track, a Triumph was coming our way now, a Triumph under the impatient hands of Jerry Wilson.

He went past without glancing toward our pit, his bike chopping them off sweetly, moving smartly along the speed groove into the south turn.

I thought of Ben's remark about a "Jerry Wilson display" and I watched Jerry steadily, studying his dirt-track technique, admiring the hot and ready sound of his machine. Mr. Ellender was partly responsible for that, but only partly. Jerry was a natural mechanic.

He made four circuits of that track at a steadily

increasing pace, handling his bike well, never varying more than a foot or two from the line he chose through the corners, his slides controlled, his stretch runs increasingly fast.

When he had pulled into the pits, I looked at Ben. Ben had been watching, too.

He said, "Sound riding."

I asked smilingly, "Where was the Jerry Wilson display?"

Ben took a breath. "That will come later, when there's some challenge. Jerry's competitive. You'll see wilder riding than that from him before this day is over."

Ben was right. I was beginning to learn that he usually is.

Chapter 10

AT PALM VISTA, motorcycle racing was properly presented and vigorously promoted. The huge, newly painted grandstand began to fill up before noon, despite the absence of any nationally known riders.

My dad came back from talking with Mr. Ellender. He looked around at all the chattering machines now filling the pits and said, "Not many Temples, are there?"

"There will be," I answered, "as soon as Johnny Burke comes to work for us."

He didn't look at me. He continued to look at all the machines in the pits as he said, "Johnny's staying with Triumph. They made him a better offer."

"Red Dunn, then?" I suggested. "Or Ed Garvey?"

"They're happy with their present arrangements," he said quietly, and looked at me. "Don't worry about it. The new Tornado we're working on will make any first-class driver a champion."

Ben said, "This sport is growing, finally. A lot of new, good boys will be coming up."

He had a point. Two seasons back a sixteen-year-old had won the Big Bear run from a field of over a thousand contestants. But when I thought of how easily Red Dunn had made a monkey out of me. . . .

My dad chuckled. "Don't look so gloomy, Tom. We're not depending on you to carry the load, not yet."

Ben Schulte winked at my dad and said lightly, "We'll be signing up Bud Briskin, probably, or Jerry Wilson."

"Stick with me and wear diamonds," I answered. "I've beat both of those two."

Only jokes in the noon sun but there was a serious strain underneath. Success in competition was a help in the promotion of motorcycle sales, as it had been in the early days of the automobile business. Motorcycles had been around for a long time but a number of Americans were only now beginning to realize what sensible transportation they were. Temple hoped to take advantage of this growing interest.

And as Temple went, so went the fortunes of the Manning family.

Three pits away, Bud Briskin was now unloading his Tornado. I went over to help him.

"Another day," he said cheerfully, "and a fast gang. But none of the big boys. I feel lucky. How do you feel?"

"Skillful. I've decided not to rely on luck. Do you think that new carburetor will make the difference?"

"What difference?"

"Do you think it will give you enough to beat me?" I paused. "For a change?"

He sighed. "Time will tell." He stared down the line of pits. "Jerry here?"

"He is."

"He's been working night and day on that machine," Bud said. "He is one determined boy, that Jerry Wilson. He's beginning to scare me."

I didn't say anything. I knew Jerry better than Bud did and had gone through many a temper tantrum with him. This one was lasting longer; I could only hope it wouldn't lead to calamity.

Bud asked, "Are they letting us try out the track?"

"Until one o'clock," I answered. "When you're through, drop over and we'll go to lunch."

I was checking the tire pressures on the Spitfire when Bud went out for his trial run. I straightened up to see this, and saw Ben take a stop watch from his jumper pocket.

I smiled. "The competition—?"

He shrugged.

Two easy laps and then Bud fanned that Tornado and Ben clicked the watch as he went by.

It was a fine display of track driving, easily among the fastest and smoothest we had seen today. When Ben clicked his watch for the second time, I looked at him questioningly.

"The carburetor helped," he answered my unspoken question.

"How fast, Ben?"

"He's a comer, that kid."

"How fast, Ben?"

"A natural. Temple has a future with lads like that riding them."

"Once more, Ben—how fast?"

"A shade under forty-two seconds," he finally answered.

That would give him a lap of between eighty-five and eighty-seven miles an hour, I figured roughly. That was *moving*. I went down to his pit to wait for him.

He idled in and ignored me for a few seconds, yawning in a hammy way, living it up.

"All right," I said. "You're good. Let's go get a couple hamburgers. I'll buy."

"Don't try to bribe me," he said.

I said, "My dad wants to know if he can have the carburetor back, now that you're through with it."

For a moment, he looked startled, and then he grinned sheepishly as I laughed.

He inhaled. "Don't do that to me. I'll buy the hamburgers and keep the carburetor."

The mammoth refreshment stand had a special counter at one end that catered only to the riders entered in today's events. We picked up our hamburgers there and took them to the picnic tables under the trees next to the parking lot.

Not far from us, Jerry and his uncle were sitting with a couple of the boys from the Oasis City Cycle Club. I was looking at Jerry when he looked at me. I waved —and he didn't.

Ben and my father came over as we were finishing our first sandwich and Ben went on to sit with Mr. Ellender. My dad stayed with us.

He said, "A forty-two-second lap, Bud. Did Tom tell you?"

"No, sir." He made a face at me. "It would have been painful, wouldn't it?"

"I didn't want to make you overconfident," I said. "You're cocky enough already."

Bud had a pencil out and was figuring on a scrap of paper. In about a minute, he said, "A forty-two-second lap figures to 85.71 miles an hour. *Now*, I'm scared."

"It was almost a tenth of a second under forty-two seconds," my dad told him. "If you're scared, think of us."

There would be four ten-mile races and a fifty-miler. Races on a mile track were limited to eight riders, so the ten-mile races were to be used as qualification trials for the half-century run. The first two finishers in each of the early races would qualify for the feature.

That track was going to be sadly tire-torn by the time the feature race topped off the day. There were bound to be some spills; I could understand now why the top rail of the fence had been removed on the turns and why we wore leather suits.

The spills in motorcycle racing are more frequent but much less damaging than spills in automobile racing. In off-track racing, they are almost expected.

And in track racing? It seemed logical to me that there would be some spills this spring Sunday at Palm Vista.

My dad came over to stand next to me. "Why so thoughtful?"

"I've been thinking about spills."

"Want to quit?"

"Not for a second. But they're a part of the sport and I've never had any practice in going down. All I know is what I read in Smith's book. He says to get away from the machine and curl into a ball."

"That's all right for scrambles," my dad said, "where there's no fence involved. But here—?"

Ben had been listening and now he said, "Here you stay away from the fence. And if the machine is heading for it, leave the machine."

"At eighty miles an hour?" I asked him.

Ben said reasonably, "You won't be heading for the fence unless you're in a slide and you won't be sliding at any speed near eighty."

They were lining up for the first ten-miler now; I would be in the third. There were two rows of four in this first race. On the outside in the second row, Jerry sat quietly on his Triumph. There was no one else in the race I knew by name, though I had seen a couple of the boys at Ventura.

It would be a standing start with the engines running, and the rumble of the eight engines was like a swarm of giant bees heard through a tunnel. The stands were quiet as the starter unfurled his white flag.

It was a fair start and a good one. All eight machines went barreling into the first turn with no machine showing a clear advantage. They were tightly bunched and moving well, all under control.

And then from the outside, near the upper fence, Jerry made a daring move, cutting straight down the bank under full acceleration. I held my breath.

He had the speed to get away with it; whether he had the legal clearance was something I was not professional enough to judge. I looked inquiringly at Ben.

Ben shrugged. "It was close, close enough to be overlooked." He continued to watch the field. "That Triumph is certainly ready."

And maybe Jerry is, too, I thought, as he led them all into the rear stretch. He had gone from last place to first in a quarter of a lap; that took something more than a hot bike.

For three laps he held that top spot while the bikes behind him engaged in their personal duels, fighting for a contending position in the dust from Jerry's Triumph.

Jerry was doing very little sliding, hardly more than the natural drift of the rear wheel as he leaned into those well-banked curves. He was riding a much headier race than I had expected from him.

And then, in the fourth lap, a lad on a Matchless came up to challenge on the outside. Jerry finally had some competition.

Easy does it now, former friend, I thought. *Don't let the challenge throw you; you've been driving an intelligent race until now.*

Down the front stretch they blasted only inches apart, both cycles under full gun, slamming into the south turn at a speed beyond any reached there in the previous laps. All three of us in our pit watched silently and fearfully.

The Matchless went into its slide first, its front wheel pointing downtrack, its rear wheel reaching for the fence. This put him behind Jerry and below him when Jerry started his slide. This put him into a fine spot for passing.

By the time Jerry had finished his slide, the Matchless had cut to the inside under power. He moved past Jerry two-thirds of the way through the corner and came out with a five-length lead.

Ben said, "That kid on the Matchless is good. He's very good."

"Jerry looks better than I thought he would," I said.

Ben smiled. "Wait." He nodded at the backstretch. "Look at him now."

We watched him bearing down on the far turn, gaining on the bike in front, but coming into that turn far too fast. He had gained half of his gap in the stretch —he lost that and more in his wild slide around the north. The stands were up and gasping as the Triumph shuddered under the sideward thrust, as it finally came under control less than a foot from the timber.

That was the story of the race, Jerry losing more on the turns than he could make up in the stretches; it was a victory of man over machine, the skill of the boy on the Matchless over the superior readiness of the Triumph. Jerry finished second only because the rest of the field was slow.

In our pit, my father looked at me.

"He'll learn," I said. "As Ben said, it will be painful, but Jerry will learn. He's far from dumb. And he *did* take second."

There were seven bikes in the second race, Bud's Temple one of the seven. Three of the riders were Amateurs, the others Novices, a tougher field than Jerry's had been.

Bud, too, took second, but a sharper second, only half a length behind the experienced man who won. I was waiting in his pit to congratulate him when he came in.

"Thank you," he said. "Your turn now. You qualify and we'll have a Dune final. How about that Jerry? He looked great for four laps. What happened to him?"

"Somebody passed him," I said. "With Jerry, that's *personal.*"

He laughed. "Oh, yes. We should know that." He looked toward the starting line. "They're getting ready. Luck, Tom. *Run your own race!*"

"I will." I tried to sound confident. "See you in the feature, champ."

Back at our pit, Ben said, "Run your own race."

"Bud just told me the same thing. What if it's not enough to place?"

My dad smiled. "So what? It can't hurt us. You're not riding a Temple." He put a hand on my shoulder. "Easy does it. No foolish chances now."

The brooding I had done about spills and the double reminder to run my own race might have been the reasons for my bad start in that ten-mile third event.

It was an eight-bike field and with three laps gone I was riding a bad eighth. Two events had already released what moisture the water truck had laid down; I rode through a dust storm.

My Spitfire was as classy as any in the field. I was giving it a bad ride. Coming into the far turn on the fourth lap, I decided this was far short of running my own race. I twisted the throttle all the way coming out, determined to learn just exactly what my limit was. It had to be better than this.

The Spitfire moved out impatiently, boring into the dust toward our first test, her knobby rear tire throwing some dust of its own. In the middle of the grandstand stretch, we caught up to a lagging Royal Enfield.

That was the model sixteen-year-old Eddie Mulder had driven to victory at Big Bear, but this wasn't Eddie Mulder. We went past before the south turn without an answering challenge.

Riding seventh now, but no bike in sight in the dust ahead. Faster through the fifth lap and, high on the far turn, one of the Oasis City boys had gone down; I was sixth. Where were the others? I could hear the chatter of their machines ahead but they were lost in the dust.

I almost ran into the man riding fifth, a Cliburn Comet and a boy from Oak Grove. He didn't relish being passed; he gunned his Comet as I started to go by on the outside.

For a full lap we paced it out and it would be comforting to relate how I finally came out on top. It wouldn't be the truth. He either had more bike or more skill or more courage. Whatever the reason, I was still riding sixth with three laps to go and I had no urge to increase my speed.

I didn't finish sixth. The leaders went down in a two-bike tangle halfway through the last lap and that automatically put the Spitfire in fourth position.

And that's where we finished, fourth. I hadn't qualified for the feature.

In our pit, my dad said, "A fine first show. Don't be gloomy."

"That was a tough field," Ben Schulte said.

I said nothing.

"You have to get used to different surfaces and different techniques," Ben went on. "You drove a very intelligent race."

"Thank you," I said.

A silence in our pit. I went to the water jug for a drink. I took off my helmet and bathed my face with a wet rag.

Bud Briskin came over to where I stood in the infield and he was grinning. "You're sulking," he said. "You had the hottest field of the day and you finished fourth. Just the luck of the draw."

"Don't be kind," I said. "I was terrible."

"No," he said. He was still grinning.

"Don't be a cocky winner," I said jokingly. I took a deep breath of the hot air. "Next time, watch out!"

"That's more like it." He looked over toward where

the fourth ten-miler was being organized, a seven-bike field. "After this one, that track is going to be treacherous. And fifty miles of that kind of going, with the cream of the field—?" He made a face.

The cream of the field. . . . He was right; only the top riders would be in the fifty-miler. Among the cream, Bud Briskin and Jerry Wilson.

But not Tom Manning. I couldn't think of anything bright to say.

Bud said, "A rough track, a fast field—and Jerry Wilson out to prove he's the hottest prospect on two wheels." He shook his head. "You're lucky to be out of it."

"I'll trade you," I said.

"Nope." He shrugged the tension from his shoulders and said quietly, "I only hope Jerry doesn't drive another race like that first one. Hold your thumbs, Tom." He went back to his pit.

Watching the fourth race, it seemed to me to be a slower field than mine had been and the time of the winner confirmed it. Perhaps, I told myself hopefully, Bud and Ben had been right; in a slower field I might have done better. I might have qualified.

We stood on our trailer in the infield to watch the final. There were two Temples in that finale, three Triumphs, two Harleys, the Cliburn Comet I had lost to and the Matchless that had whipped Jerry, the eight top bikes of the day.

It was a hot field, a rough track and a great show. Bud and a rider from Bakersfield, an experienced Amateur on a Harley-Davidson, tangled for the lead right from the start, setting an early pace that gave them a quarter-lap lead on the third bike after five laps.

Ben said to my father, "That Briskin is a fine dirt-track competitor. If we don't line up one of the big boys before long, he might not be a bad choice for this kind of racing."

Resentment stirred in me faintly. I said nothing.

My father said, "And Tom for the scrambles? Let's not forget our boy." He winked at me.

Ben said calmly, "I'm not likely to forget Tom. For promotion we need a *team,* not a single star."

From the ruck now, the Dune Dynamo, Wild Jerry Wilson, came charging up to make his bid. His sanity might be questioned, but the readiness of his machine and his own personal courage were at full peak today. Despite the time-consuming violence of his slides, he was gaining on the leaders.

And the crowd loved him for the mechanized cowboy he was; they gave him a standing ovation every time he came around.

Ben Schulte shook his head sadly. My father's eyes were bleak. I remembered Bud's asking me to hold my thumbs and I gripped them rigidly.

In front, the Temple and the Harley were still at it nose to nose, neither bike gaining an advantage for long. A quarter of a lap behind them was the Cliburn Comet and Jerry was closing in on him as the Comet came sliding out into the grandstand straightaway.

The duel for first place was a better show but the

crowd seemed to prefer the showboating fireworks of
Jerry Wilson's bid for third. He was the man who
kept them standing and drew their cheers.

I thought of Mr. Ellender in the pits and hoped
Jerry's mother wasn't here to witness this.

Past our pit the Comet was still in the lead with
Jerry gaining, and it was logical to expect the Oak
Grove boy would regain his gap on the turn. He'd
been too tough a man on the turns for me.

He wasn't too tough for Jerry. Jerry stole the lead
on that turn exactly the same as he had in the ten-
miler, swinging high, gunning his power-packed machine to the limit and cutting sharply downtrack. He
came out of the bend in front and took off after the
dueling pair leading the parade.

"Whew!" Ben Schulte said, and wiped the back of
his neck.

My dad said, "I'm almost glad you're not in this one,
Tom."

I smiled. "I am, too—*almost*. What does Jerry
have, Ben?"

"Determination," he said. "It's also called stubborn-
ness. When I had it, my friends called it bullheaded-
ness."

My dad laughed nervously, his eyes on the streaking Triumph. "Charley's a fair mechanic, but the condition of that machine could only be Jerry's work.
He's a natural engineer, that boy. He should be in
college."

Ben said, "Charley was willing to send him. But

maybe that's too easy a way for Jerry to learn. Well, let's hope he stays in one piece today."

Jerry stayed in one piece but his machine was only steel, aluminum and rubber. It burned up a valve on the thirty-seventh lap and the fans could sit down again.

The boy on the Harley won it by less than ten feet over Bud Briskin, a dogfight right up to the checkered flag.

For the second time that afternoon, I went over to congratulate Bud. I wondered when it would be his turn.

Chapter 11

I HADN'T won a race yet so there wasn't any reason for me to feel bad about losing at Palm Vista. But it bothered me and I wondered if it was because both Jerry and Bud had done better. Nobody likes to lose, even though I knew Ben and my dad hadn't been looking for a victory, only another chance at experience in competition.

Two weeks later, there was a short-track race at Ansco and I once more finished poorly. Maybe, I told myself, I was better equipped for the cross-country stuff. Jerry hadn't been at Ansco; Bud took two seconds, the best Novice record at the meet.

Again, Ben Schulte kept a watchful eye on Bud and I could tell he was impressed by what he saw. Bud Briskin was developing into a first-class track rider.

At school, I told him, "I'm getting a Jerry Wilson complex about you. I guess nobody gets used to losing, right?"

"I'm losing," he said. "Not to you, but always to somebody. And once you get me out in the rough going I'll probably lose to you again." He grinned. "Maybe you need a Temple Tornado."

"The way I'm doing," I told him, "I may never get one unless I buy it."

"You're doing all right," he said seriously. "Stop sulking; you're a college man now." He sighed. "I'm not crying, even though the boys are beginning to call me 'Second-place Briskin.' It's still fun, Tom, win or lose."

He had a point. It was exciting, challenging, a sport that demanded the best physically and mentally from a man, and I was too young to win in the class of company I had chosen. I tried to develop a more reasonable attitude.

Bud had taken four consecutive seconds in his last four events. That might look like a fine record to me because I hadn't done as well. But it must have been frustrating to Bud and I'd never heard him complain.

June eighth I finished my first year at Western Tech. On June tenth, American Temple brought out the new competitive Temple Tornado.

The frame had been lightened, though strengthened, and Dad had redesigned the combustion chamber and developed a hotter ignition system that added five horsepower to the machine.

Walter Devlin had been going around the country and had lined up a few new dealers, but both he and my father felt that the publicity of competitive victories was still the most successful promotion for our product. Motorcycle riders were sport-minded, and not inclined to give too much attention to advertising media, such as TV and magazines.

The Saturday after the introduction of the new Tornado there was a meeting in Dad's office. My dad and

Mr. Devlin and Ben Schulte and the publicity man from Devlin Engines were there. And so was I.

The publicity man explained he had been unsuccessful in signing any of the top riders; they were all satisfied with their present associations.

Ben Schulte handed Mr. Devlin a list of the better Amateurs and Novices he had noticed since returning to the sport. Mr. Devlin explained that there would be a limited production for this year and the dealer organization already established should be able to sell most of it.

"For next year," he went on, "we have more ambitious sales and production plans." I thought he looked at me as he said, "The last half of this year, we hope to prepare for that expansion, to make ourselves ready for it."

And now he not only looked at me, he addressed me. "Tom, you look uncomfortable."

"I've been wondering why I'm here, sir," I said.

"You should be able to guess." He was smiling.

I said, "Maybe I worded that wrong. What I've really been wondering is whether I'd be here if my father wasn't vice-president of American Temple."

They all laughed.

Mr. Devlin said, "It's possible you might not. But it's more than possible that your father wouldn't be here if you hadn't given him an interest in motorcycles. We think we've developed a superior competitive machine. If you don't work out this year, you and young Briskin, we can try again for one of the more famous riders next season."

Bud, too. . . . I could feel a tightness growing between my shoulder blades, at the base of my neck. *If you don't work out this year.* . . .

My dad said, "Well, Tom—? Nothing to say?"

I took a deep breath. Finally, I said, "Let's hope I work out. I'm sure Bud will."

Bud and I weren't the only two involved in this promotional scheme, I learned later. There were two promising Amateurs in the Middle West, one in the South and three in the East who had agreed to try out the new Tornado in their campaigns this summer. They weren't given machines for nothing, but they were offered them at a price too reasonable to turn down. The loss would be charged to advertising by American Temple.

Bud Briskin wondered why his old Temple wouldn't do as well. He didn't wonder long; he tried out the new one and sold his a day later. At a loss, for a change—that's how enthused he was.

Every important meet west of the Rockies not restricted to Experts would be our battleground. We were assured more than once that we weren't expected to win any big races, not this year; this would be a year of learning. I was sure, however, that we were expected to look like potential winners.

We were entered in two meets in July. One was a half-mile dirt-track meet at Middleton, the other a Tourist Trophy run near San Diego. The San Diego run was a Four Star meet and there would be some superior competition there.

We didn't expect to run into as impressive a group

at Middleton, and we didn't. In the feature, Bud came home with his first win, no longer "Second-place Briskin." And Tom Manning? Painfully but clearly the fact was coming home to me that I wasn't likely to become a winner on the dirt tracks. I took a bad fourth and a worse fifth. I finished in these ignoble positions riding what seemed to be the cream of the field.

In the pit, after the second of my humiliations for the day, I sat glumly on the machine and stared at Ben Schulte, waiting for his critique.

"She didn't sound quite right," he said. "Maybe the mag—?"

I shook my head. "The mag's fine. Let's face it—she sounded better than I looked."

He nodded in agreement. "So? You'll improve. And that's one reason you and Bud are both riding Temples, Bud for the track racing and you for the off-track racing. Some of our biggest riders never mastered both fields."

"I want to, Ben."

"Sure you do," he said reasonably. "And wouldn't it be a wonderful world if we all got what we wanted?"

In the next pit, my dad was working with Bud, getting ready for the feature which Bud later won. Ben went over to lend a hand.

I went to the water jug, feeling childishly sorry for myself, and the thought of Jerry Wilson came to mind. Jerry, the bad loser; I was beginning to feel more empathy for him. Who likes to lose?

My dad left Bud's pit and came over to where I stood. He asked, "Sulking? The race is over."

"I know. I think I hate to lose as much as Jerry does."

"Naturally," he said. "But the discipline is in not showing it. And trying to learn from each loss. That's why you're here, to learn."

"I know, Pop, I know. Well, maybe at San Diego—"

At San Diego, there would be no water splash or mud bog. (They were barred from TT competition.) But there was no doubt in my mind that the going would be rugged without these added hazards.

It would be my first try at off-track racing since Ventura, and that had been too many months back for me to regain the confidence I'd been losing this year.

I came to San Diego with a bad attitude, too determined to maintain the poise and discipline any type of motorcycle racing requires. I was tight as the bark on a tree, jittery and fretful.

Ben Schulte's experienced eyes didn't overlook the indications of my nervousness. He said quietly, "If you're not ready, don't race. No meet is important enough to risk your getting hurt."

"I'll be ready," I promised. "It's the waiting that makes me nervous. Once the race is under way, I'll be all right."

He studied me carefully but made no comment.

About ten feet away, Bud and my dad were tinkering with Bud's cycle and Bud didn't seem nervous. Fifty feet away, my former friend, Jerry Wilson, was joking with some boys from Ventura. He looked at me and past me, his eyes blank.

Dune was long ago and far away. And nobody was singing *Auld Lang Syne.* We were in a new world, competitive and demanding.

Ben Schulte said quietly, "It's still a sport. If you don't enjoy it you're foolish to indulge in it. What's wrong, Tom?"

"Jerry Wilson, for one thing," I said. "And my own lack of skill for another. Don't worry about me, Ben; I'll grow up."

He said, "Don't ever grow up if it's going to make your life less interesting. That's what happened to me." He paused. "Until you and that Spitfire brought me back to my youth."

"That's another angle," I said, "the Spitfire. I know that was a great scrambler. But this Tornado—?"

"Is better," he said. "You'll see."

Bud came over to ask me, "You hungry, sourpuss? I'm starved."

"I guess I can eat." I looked at Ben.

"Your dad and I will eat later," he said, "with Walter Devlin."

So *he* was going to be here. . . . If you don't work out this year. . . .

We rode over to the restaurant in Ben's Plymouth. On the way, Bud said, "Devlin here? We'd better be hot. Feel lucky, Tom?"

"Nope. I feel like an All-American loser."

"Snap out of it," he said. "If they take those Tornadoes away from us, we'll buy a pair of Harleys and run 'em out of the game."

I laughed. "Easy, boy. That would put my dad back into the air-conditioning business."

We rode for a few blocks in silence. Then he said, "You're feeling all right, aren't you? You don't seem —well."

"I'm all right physically. Oh, it's—a combination of things."

Another silence, and then, "Jerry Wilson, for instance?"

"A part of it. Jeepers—we grew up together!"

Bud sighed. And then, just as he parked in front of the restaurant, he said, "You and I on new Temples— that is the deepest cut of all to Jerry. He's been sounding off around the Dune Diner about that. He's out to make us look bad."

"Worse riders on slower machines have been doing that to me," I said. "Jerry will have to stand in line."

We didn't talk much during the lunch. I had a feeling Bud wasn't in sympathy with my negative attitude and there was no reason why he should be. As Ben had said, if I didn't enjoy it I should get out of it. Nobody was forcing me to race.

We were back at the course only a few minutes after noon and Bud asked, "How about a practice run together? You follow my line the first trip around; I'll follow yours the second."

We kicked our mounts into life and I followed him as he swung around and headed out toward the level field that made up the first quarter of the course. With the Tornado barking cleanly and the bite of those knobby tires giving us perfect traction, some of my depression evaporated. I studied Bud's line as we swung onto the old fire trail that led to the first climb.

There wasn't much to see, as yet, but I watched his rear wheel as he leaned on the wide turn, studying the action of the rear fork, checking the possibility of lost traction on bumpy surfaces. Dad had built a heavier shock absorber into the rear swinging arm for off-track models; the track model had a rigid rear frame. The track model was also made without brakes; the machines we were riding now had completely enclosed nine-inchers.

The old fire trail wandered to the right here, the course cut sharply to the left and we were climbing on loose shale, a steep climb and shifting footage but the Tornadoes went steadily up like the little thoroughbreds they were.

At the top of the hill, we could see the ocean, the curving line of the bay and the whitecaps, and to the south we could see the town spread out. We were back on the discarded fire trail and the going was smooth and Bud took off with a twist of the wrist.

Ahead I could see the sign that signaled an abrupt S-curve. To me it seemed as though Bud was going into it too fast. I gave him a little more clearance and got ready to shift down to third.

He had figured it wrong. Only a desperate braking slide and some inspired handling kept him upright and on course. I went into third gear and breezed through it like a Garvey.

This was what I needed; this was my kind of going.

I gave him a forty-foot lead and watched his every move, studying the trail to see if there was a better line than the one he was showing me.

Into a rocky arroyo now, where a careless turn could smash a front wheel, into third gear again as we began to climb out of it, back to the trail again and smooth going.

A half-mile of top-gear travel, almost full throttle, and then a dip—and a jump.

Soaring, my first air trip on the Tornado. She took it better than my Spitfire had; that heavy rear shock dampener absorbing the jolt of landing without passing it on to the saddle.

A downhill run and a sweeping left turn with adverse camber, the rear wheel trying to slide out to the right and down the bank, but the traction held. Below us, about half a mile away, we could see the finish line.

A sweeping right turn, a sharp left—and a plowed field.

Down to third I shifted, down to second. That sweet Tornado went through this heavy going with power to spare, no sign of strain. Dad had added enough horses, that much seemed certain.

Over the crusted furrows, the rear wheel never spinning, the front-wheel dampener lessening the jerk on the handlebars. Over the last furrow to a quarter mile of flat, hard surface leading to the finish line.

At the line, Bud slowed to let me by and followed my lead for the second trip.

I won't bore you with the details. I will say with an

alarming lack of modesty that most of my confidence, lost on the dirt tracks, was coming back through this rural travel. I will add that I'm sure the second trip was made at a faster pace than the first, though I will admit that familiarity helped the second time around.

When we came in our elders were back from their lunch. My dad asked, "Well—?"

I made a circle with thumb and forefinger. "Perfect. It's a real scrambler."

"It's 30 per cent better than my old bike," Bud added. "You're a genius, Mr. Manning."

My dad grinned and looked at Mr. Devlin. "Hear that, Walter? No more arguments this week on whether we're ready?"

Mr. Devlin smiled and made no comment. Ben Schulte went over to get the gas can. I went over to get a drink of water.

"You look happier," Ben said. "I figured you might. Tom, if you don't mind a little blunt speech, I don't think you'll ever be a track rider of any importance. This is your field, as it was mine."

I didn't argue with him. I wasn't qualified to argue with Ben Schulte. But I reserved the quiet opinion that even he could be wrong.

"You have a fine judgment for surface, for traction," he went on. "For this kind of racing, that's very important—and quite rare. Don't try to be *everything*, Tom."

"I won't," I said. "I don't want to be an aviator or a bus driver or even a beautician. I only want to be a *complete* motorcycle rider."

"Oh, Tom—" he said sadly. "Young people—" He went back to the others, carrying the gas can.

I drank two paper cups of water slowly, thinking of Walter Devlin and my dad's remark about being "ready." Was it the Tornado or its riders that Mr. Devlin didn't consider "ready"? We weren't supposed to be, not yet. He had said that very thing in my dad's office. He must have meant the new Tornado and he was wrong on that. It was *ready*.

And then, as I stood there, a familiar figure came walking across the flat area behind the motorcycles, heading my way. It was the tall, thin figure of Mr. Ellender.

"How are you, Tom?" he asked me quietly.

"Fine, thank you, Mr. Ellender. You're certainly looking good."

"But troubled," he said. "Jerry's being—absurd, Tom. But I had to talk with you. You're doing very well, and so is Bud. I'm happy to see it."

"Thank you. Jerry's stubborn, Mr. Ellender, but he's not hopeless. Think of the hundreds of times we fought. And he *always* came around later. I haven't given up on him."

"Neither have I," he said quietly. "You were a good influence on him, Tom. I'm heartened to hear you're not bitter about the way he's acting." He went on, to talk with the others.

Bud came over to pour a cup of water. He drank it and poured another. He didn't look at me. "That Mr. Ellender's been a real father to Jerry, hasn't he?"

"He's been a saint," I said. "Oh, that Jerry has some lumps coming—"

Bud shrugged. "He's in the right game for it. Well, we've got enough problems of our own." He paused. "One of mine is learning to beat you in this kind of race."

"Follow me," I said, "and learn. Let's get ready, track star."

There would be no preliminary heats or elimination trials today, only the feature, ten laps of this five-and-a-half-mile course, fifty-five miles of varied terrain and surface to test all of a driver's skills.

On the block-long starting line, I was placed next to a man I knew, Bruce Cady from Oasis City. He looked over and grinned. "I hear your buddy took a first at Middleton."

"That's right. That's his kind of going, dirt track."

"How'd you do there? Were you there?"

"I was there. I didn't do so well." I returned his grin. "But today's another day."

A pause, and then he added, "I don't know if you know it, but Jerry Wilson's in our club now."

I nodded. "Jerry will shape up."

A pause, and then, "What happened between you two?"

"Ask Jerry. I guess— I don't know."

The longest pause of all. "Well, we all wanted you to know we think a lot of you and Bud Briskin and we know Jerry can be unreasonable. I hope that doesn't sound like a speech; the boys in the OCCC wanted you two to hear our sentiments."

"Thanks," I said. "I'll tell Bud." I took a breath. "And with Jerry, you'll need some patience, but I've always thought of him as a first-class guy, just the same."

"We know that. And that's why we took him in. Luck, Tom."

"To all of us," I agreed. "We need it."

Skill? Naturally. A hot machine? Of course. Poise, confidence? Certainly. And a little luck, the extra ingredient we all need when our skill and our machines and our attitudes have put us into a position where a little luck will make the difference.

All eyes on the white flag now, raised in the starter's hand. It dropped and the Tornado was moving before the flag finished its fall.

I had the machine, my attitude had improved. The skill and the luck? We would see. Bruce dropped behind as the Tornado went streaking out over the level field toward the deserted fire trail that led to the shale-strewn hill.

Only two bikes beat me to that trail. Two bikes out of a field of fifty; that had been the machine, not Manning. Any fool can twist a throttle.

First of the boys in front of me was Jed Levy, one of the finest Amateurs on the Pacific Coast. The other man I didn't know, but from where I sat he seemed to know his business. I gave the second man twenty feet and followed his lead.

He was riding a Cliburn, and as soon as we turned off onto the shale it was clear to me that he didn't have the traction the Tornado was giving me. I didn't pass; I filed the information for possible future use. I let him keep his lead.

Up, up, up—and now the ocean and the town were in view in the distance and we were back on the fire trail with smooth flat going ahead. Jed took off like a rocket and the Cliburn followed.

I had more than enough power under me to match their pace, but I didn't. I kept them in sight and let them gain another fifty feet. I knew Jed was far more experienced than I was and guessed that the man on the Cliburn Comet was almost his equal.

The S-curve now and I was down to third without waiting to see how they played it. I knew *my* limits. They showed me a line through that double turn neither Bud nor I had used, a better line coming out of the final curve in good position for the trail to the arroyo.

Learn, learn, learn, Tom Manning—your superiors are teaching you without even knowing it.

Into the arroyo and the rocks looked bigger and the path we followed seemed to have grown narrower. This was no time to watch the men ahead; threading between those jagged rocks kept my attention geared to the clearance the machine needed.

Climbing now, up over the rim, onto the trail and a half-mile of very little less than full throttle. The gap to the second-place rider remained constant and I had a feeling his bike was all out. Jed gained only a few feet on both of us.

The dip. The jump. What a bike my dad had built,

soaring like a glider, landing like a butterfly. He and Ben were right; a man could defeat his superiors on a bike like this. I had plenty of superiors.

The downhill run, the left turn with treacherous camber. How that Jed handled it! He kept his Triumph under perfect control and at a speed I didn't dare to attempt. He gained on both of us as we came sweeping down toward the plowed field.

I had gone to second here on my trial run; this trip I gambled on third gear. The traction was firm, the new bigger dampeners kept the bike on an even keel. I picked up all the ground I had lost on the downhill run.

The flat stretch that led to the line, and I went back to the pillion, bending low over the tank, as we went to top gear and full throttle.

I didn't keep it at full throttle. A few hundred yards at that speed convinced me I could have taken both bikes ahead right here and now. That wasn't my plan. Once I had the knowledge of my mount's ability, passing could wait. This pair ahead still had some things to teach me.

I kept my eyes glued toward the line of pits, looking for Ben's red-and-yellow-checked jacket. I must have been doing well over ninety when I flashed by him.

He had his arms stretched to the utmost, his palms flat, his fingers reaching. I had more than an adequate lead on the man directly behind, that meant.

What more did I need? The men ahead were in sight, the men behind still out of challenging position. My ego didn't demand a victory here; the tenth lap would do as well.

And where, I wondered, was Bud Briskin? Where was that dirt-track flash? You will pardon, I hope, this momentary smugness; it had been so long since I could afford a touch of smugness.

For two laps this euphoria continued. And then, on the third lap, Jed began to move away and the man on the Cliburn followed. It was a moment of decision for me and I decided not to follow immediately. I was already traveling at a speed very close to my limit.

They were soon out of sight. As I went past the pits, Ben signaled that the pair ahead had a larger gap on me than I had on the rider behind. I didn't look back to see the man behind. The Tornado's pace increased; my confidence still strong.

For a full lap no competitor was in sight; I could have been the last man in the world. And then on the fifth, as I threaded between the rocks in the arroyo, I heard the bark of another bike close behind.

Out of the arroyo, back to smooth going at full throttle, not looking behind, trusting the Tornado to lengthen the lead on my unknown challenger.

The dip, the jump—and again the sound of a cycle coming up as we streaked into the downhill turn. A wide reverse turn, the sharp left and the plowed ground.

Here, I was sure, the sound from behind would grow fainter. To my right, a bike had gone down and the driver was trying to lift it back into the action. It wasn't Levy or the boy on the Cliburn; it had to be someone I was lapping. The sound from behind didn't fade.

Through the quarter mile of smooth going, the sound neither increased nor diminished. Ben Schulte's signal told me there was a rider close behind, something I'd known longer than Ben had.

Throughout the entire lap that followed, the sound of my pursuer was constant. We passed some bikes that were stalled or spilled; we lapped two that were moving, but caught no glimpse of the two ahead that were leading.

It wasn't until the seventh lap we caught up with the Cliburn Comet. It had smashed a wheel in the arroyo; its driver was unhurt, standing next to his mount, looking woefully down at it.

I was in second place and only one challenger behind, so far as I could tell. On the flat ground beyond the jump, I stole a glance to the rear.

My pursuer was Jerry Wilson.

If it had been anyone else, I'm sure I wouldn't have reacted as competitively as I did. I sent the Tornado up into a speed range I wasn't prepared to handle.

Luck must have been with me for the first lap at this new pace. The Tornado stayed upright; Jerry didn't gain an inch, so far as I could tell.

It was on the last lap, threading through the rocks, that I realized first place was out of the question now, unless Levy had gone into the pits unnoticed by me. He hadn't been stranded anywhere on the course and I hadn't passed him.

I was a cinch for second, unless Jerry made his move in the next two miles. On the stretch before the finish line, he wouldn't have the horses to overtake the Tornado.

The jump and the downhill run.

And here, on this treacherous curve with the bad camber, I decided to eliminate Jerry's remote chance to overtake me before the checkered flag.

I went into that turn like a fool—and the rear wheel started to slide before I could compensate with a weight shift. The front wheel swung uphill; the rear spun wildly; I was out of control, heading backward down the slope, all traction gone on the slippery grass outside the course.

I jumped, to get away from the machine, as Jerry swept by above.

Chapter 12

"No BROKEN bones," the intern said. "I guess he'll be all right without a trip to the hospital."

I was sitting on a cot next to the ambulance on the parking lot and I had just been checked over. I felt bruised and nauseous but more important than that, I felt like a fool. I had blown a cinch second place.

Levy had won. Jerry Wilson was second. Bud had finished in sixth place.

My father said, "A part of the game. You ran a fine race for nine and a half laps."

"Until I saw Jerry," I added.

Ben Schulte said nothing, but I remembered he had warned me to ride my own race and I could guess he was thinking of that now. Even if Jerry had gone past me on that slope, I probably would have caught him again on the final stretch run, or through that plowed area.

Walter Devlin had gone back to town. I was glad of that! I stood up shakily as Bud came over with Bruce Cady.

"What happened?" he asked. "I just heard about your spill. Are you all right? And the bike?"

"They're both repairable," my dad said easily.

"I was trying to show up Jerry Wilson," I said. "I rode that last hill too fast. Congratulations on the finish."

"Sixth?" he said. "That's not so great."

Bruce said, "Jerry didn't crowd you on that hill, did he, Tom?"

"Not for a second," I said. "He was forty yards behind me when I started to slide."

Bud and Bruce both stared. Bud said wonderingly, "Forty yards—? What— I mean—"

"I guess," I admitted, "I have the same fault Jerry has; too much competitive spirit. It was just—stupid! I goofed it."

They were both smiling now. And Bud said, "You sure did. Well, you looked great for over nine-tenths of the race. You'll have to admit that's an improvement, Tom."

Resentment glimmered briefly in me and then I managed to dredge up a smile and give him the good-loser's line. "Next time," I promised.

I learned, that summer and fall, that it's easier to be a good loser on the outside than inside. I didn't exactly resent the boys who were beating me, but I doubt if I would have voted for them in a popularity contest.

In the off-track meets, I did better than Bud but came home with no firsts. In the track racing, Bud continued to improve. He won a time-trial short-track preliminary at Big Oak and took a fine second in the fifty-mile feature race at Bay City.

In the Sierra Scrambles, I nosed out Jerry Wilson in a last-lap dogfight to take fourth place and temporarily assuage the humiliation of my defeat at San Diego.

Jerry's riding had improved tremendously; I had no

doubt that he would have beaten me that day if he'd been mounted on one of our new Tornadoes.

In a TT at Juniper, Nevada, he came back to take a third to my fifth when I left the course for a nine-second lapse after trying to span a reverse turn too fast. The top ten finishers had really been bunched at Juniper; I had been second when I left the course.

The resentment I was trying not to show must have become noticeable to Ben Schulte. He told me, "You're trying too hard. You're tense. What's bothering you?"

"Losing," I answered. "Who likes to lose?"

"Nobody. But in a fifty-bike scrambles, forty-nine riders lose. Think of some of the riders you've been beating." He paused. "And don't make a career out of beating Jerry Wilson."

"I'm not."

"All right, I'll only say you're making it more important than it should be. You'll have to be beating better riders than Jerry by this time next year. Your dad has come up with the machine to do it; the rest depends on you and Bud."

At the Sacramento State Fair, Bud finally had a chance to go up against some of the nation's top riders. In a hundred miles of test against a field of far greater individual experience, only one man beat Bud Briskin to the checkered flag. And that man was Johnny Burke.

Johnny came over to the pit after the race to look over our machines, and he said ruefully to my dad, "I guess

I made a bad decision, didn't I? You've come up with a winner."

"I'm almost ready to unveil the new one," my dad told him. "It will be a little faster."

Johnny shook his head. "This one's too fast, already. Well, Triumph is coming out with a new one, too. If this sport is going to grow, we need the competition." He winked at me. "Better luck next time, Tom."

I hadn't even qualified for the hundred-miler. I was still a complete dud at track racing.

Johnny hadn't been the first of the big riders who had admired the new Temple. And the thought came to me that perhaps some of the others would be receptive now to offers from the firm. Temple Tornadoes were doing very well all over the country and they were not being ridden by Experts. Some of the Experts could be wondering how *they* would do on this new winner.

Bud was living up to what Mr. Devlin had a right to expect from the new machines. Was I?

At Phoenix, in November, I had my chance to go up against some of the big boys. Jerry Wilson wasn't there and that might have been why I felt less tense and more confident than I had all fall.

Again, as I had at Ventura, I used Ed Garvey as my pilot for the first few laps. It was a rugged desert and mountain course the Phoenix MC had laid out for this Tourist Trophy competition, and cautious Ed Garvey was a safe man to follow.

In the middle of the third lap, I moved past him. There were at least a half-dozen riders in front of him and the way Ed was going, I doubted if he'd ever catch any of them.

It was a good day for me; I had never ridden better. I suppose it helped that Red Dunn ripped a tire and Johnny Burke burned out a valve on the last lap, but there were still some giants at the meet who finished upright—and behind me.

They all finished behind me—I had achieved my first victory.

In the pit, Ben Schulte said, "It had to happen. You were overdue, boy. Fine race."

"And a superior bike," I added.

My father gripped my shoulder. "That isn't enough. You were great. Poise, discipline, imagination—you showed it all."

And now some of the big boys were coming over to congratulate me. At least that was their excuse, but I noticed they all spent time studying that Tornado, and looking thoughtful.

Ben whispered to me, "I'll bet we could sign up half of them right now."

Bud, who had finished fifth, said quietly, "You ought to grab one to take my place."

Ben said, "You're our track winner, Bud. We can't afford to lose you."

"That's not as exciting as this," Bud said. "Even an automobile can race on a track. This is the true cycle sport."

Bud Briskin, the winner. . . . And there had been disappointment in his voice. To me, Bud had been the ace in this team. Had he thought *I* was?

And for the thousandth time, I thought of Jerry Wilson, who hated to lose and admitted it. We were all brothers; were we less than he because we wouldn't admit we hated to lose?

Jerry was no longer a wild driver, and the Oasis City CC might have been partly responsible for that. But only partly; Jerry was too stubborn a boy to accept advice with which he didn't agree. If he had outgrown his wildness, couldn't he outgrow his resentment?

I hoped so; I missed Jerry Wilson.

Two meets were canceled in December because of rain; in the East there would be no more meets until late spring.

In January, Bud told me at school that he had heard that three of last year's top ten riders were interested in riding for Temple.

At home, that evening, I asked my dad how true this rumor was.

He told me it was the truth.

"And Mr. Devlin—?" I asked. "I'll bet he wants to accept them and you don't."

My dad shook his head. "Don't you remember that I had to put up all that money before I could come into the firm? Mr. Devlin, you must not forget, has a memory." He smiled. "He told the boys the machines were for sale to anyone, but we already had a fine group of factory riders."

"He sounds like Jerry Wilson," I said. "He can't expect those boys to risk their reputations on an untried machine."

"He holds no grudges," my father said. "Think of it this way—he's being loyal to you and Bud and the other lads who took a chance."

I took a deep breath. "I thought he was more practical than that."

"And consider this, too," my father explained. "If Red Dunn or Burke or Garvey win, the fan might assume it's their skill that won, not the machines. But if Amateurs win on Temples—?"

"It's not skill?"

He laughed. "Let's call it a happy combination—man and machine."

And luck? At Phoenix, Red Dunn and Johnny Burke had been stopped by machine failure. They had been the hottest riders there; they had been ahead of me when forced out. Bud and I had passed the test, we were Temple men. I felt Bud had earned it more than I had.

When I told him about my conversation with Dad he looked as doubtful as I felt. "Think we're big enough?" he asked me.

"Nope. But who am I to argue with the great Walter Devlin?"

He grinned. "Cheer up, Tom—it's not our money."

True enough. And it seemed reasonable to guess Walter Devlin didn't get to be a millionaire by making mistakes about money. All we could do was our best and hope it would be enough.

In February I finished a sad fourth in a twenty-five-miler at Los Gatos. Bud was leading the parade until a faulty primary chain had broken on the twenty-fourth lap. Temple didn't look so good that day.

I won a moto-cross in Fresno a week later, but there hadn't been too much competition and not a single nationally known rider. Bud came in second, his best to date in off-track racing.

And then the rains came back with a vengeance. Our average for a season out here is about fifteen inches of rain. We had twelve inches in March, seventeen straight days of downfall. Added to our six inches in December, we were already above the seasonal average.

On a rainy Saturday afternoon, we had a meeting once more in my father's office and this time Bud was there, too.

There were two topics to be discussed, the new Tornado and the Sagebrush Scrambles. This last-named could be a very important event for the American Temple Company. Because it was being moved up to May, to coincide with a motorcycle dealers' convention in Palm Springs and it was certain most of the dealers would attend.

"We want to show well there," Mr. Devlin pointed out, "and I'm wondering how you boys feel about riding the new machines."

Both Bud and I stared at him blankly, not sure of what he meant.

"You're used to last year's model," he explained, "and there won't be many meets before the Sagebrush for you to get used to the new bike." He looked out the window. "If this rain continues, there won't be *any*."

I looked at Bud and Bud looked at me. I asked, "How different is the new model going to be?"

"More powerful," he said. "A shade heavier. We'll have a few pilot models ready by the first of next week."

Bud suggested, "Why don't we try them next week? We can decide after that. It still gives us time for the Pine Valley Run before the Sagebrush."

Mr. Devlin asked, "And if it rains all next week—?"

Bud smiled confidently. "It can't, Mr. Devlin. There's no more water left up there."

Walter Devlin laughed and looked at my father and then at Ben Schulte. "Well, gentlemen—?"

Ben Schulte said, "You're the gambler, Walter—you decide."

Mr. Devlin looked at Bud and grinned. "I didn't decide. You did. You'd better be right, young man."

Bud's crystal ball was unclouded; the rain stopped Sunday night and the April sun came out in full force on Monday. A little after four o'clock Monday afternoon we had the new models out on the five acres of unimproved land behind the Devlin Engine Company.

It had been used by the American Temple engineers before, and they had built a few jumps and a rough trail along a slope near the drainage district. It wasn't a true Tourist Trophy course by any means but it was adequate to test the performance factors of the new bikes.

It was muddy going, except near the drainage canal. It wasn't a complete test, as I've said, but it was enough of a test to encourage us. The traction was improved, the engines more immediately responsive. As we came idling back to the engineers' shack, Bud looked over at me questioningly.

I nodded and patted the tank of my machine. Dad came out to meet us. He, too, had a question in his eyes.

"We like 'em," Bud said simply. "Are they ready to roll?"

Dad nodded. "You're sure, now?"

Bud paused; he didn't want to make the decision, I could see.

I said, "We can try them at Pine Valley. If they don't work out, we'll go back to our old machines for the Sagebrush."

"Good," Bud said quickly. "This time it was *your* decision."

The Pine Valley Run was a new meet and hadn't built enough prestige as yet to attract the bright stars. With our new machines untried in competition, Bud and I were happy with that situation.

I still felt I had been lucky at Phoenix; a warm-up run before meeting those same stars again in the Sagebrush might help to nourish my ego.

There were some fine bikes at Pine Valley, just the same, and some competent boys as eager and determined as we were. The course itself was not only scenic, it was designed to test a rider's skill and minimize the success of uncontrolled top speed.

I expected to see Jerry Wilson there but one of the

boys from the OCCC told me he was getting his bike ready for the Sagebrush.

"That's the one he wants to win," the OCCC boy said. "That's his old stamping grounds around there." A pause. "Yours, too, isn't it?"

I nodded. Then, "Jerry's racing better than ever, isn't he? He's not as—wild as he used to be."

The lad grinned. "We slowed him down. He always had the potential. He'll never be the *perfect* loser, though."

Neither will Tom Manning, I thought. And who would want to compete for *that* title? Somebody always has to lose, of course, but I was happier when it was somebody *else.*

My dad came over to stand next to me and we looked up at the trail cut through the forest, the wandering, climbing trail that was the start of the Pine Valley Run.

"How's business?" I asked him. "Are we making out?"

"Better every day. Even if we weren't, I'm not sure it would be too important. Tom, for the first time in a dozen years, I'm enjoying my work. I get up every morning and look forward to the day. That doesn't show in a bank account, but some day you'll learn how important it is."

"I've learned it already," I told him. "Put everybody on two wheels, that's our aim. Forward with American Temple!"

He laughed and went over to greet Bud, arriving with Ben.

Forward with Crispie Crunchies. . . . I thought

back to Dune and all the desert days with Jerry Wilson and that silly blood-brother oath. I thought of the fun we'd had and the fights, the camping trips, the search for lost mines, that battered old Harley. If losing Jerry was a part of growing up, I was sorry to see time pass.

I did all right at Pine Valley that day. I didn't win; and perhaps I could have if I had tried a little harder, extended the limits of my present skill a shade, used the full power of that new Tornado, taken some risks that I refused to take.

I finished second behind Bruce Cady and didn't mind. I knew what the machine could do now, what I could do, and I hoped both of us would combine to let the boys at the Sagebrush know that American Temple was the comer, the bike to beat.

Bud finished fourth and was almost as content as I was. He, too, had decided to use this race as a tightener, preparing himself for the bigger Sunday to come, back in our old home ground.

Chapter 13

COMING INTO town from the west, the desert was in bloom from all the rain we'd had, and Dune looked fresh and clean. We stopped at Ben and Ed's Filling Station and Mr. Haskins told us Ben had gone to pick up a car but would be back in about fifteen minutes.

I told my dad, "I'm going to run over to the Dune Diner. I haven't seen Barney and Joe since they came to Los Angeles for the auto show."

"You'd better eat while you're there," my dad said. "I don't know what the facilities will be at the Sagebrush."

It had been over a year since I'd seen Barney and Joe and longer than that since I'd entered their diner. They were still a pair of hams.

Barney's eyes went wide as I opened the door and he pretended to be clutching his heart in great shock. At the griddle, Joe said, "It can't be! This is too marvelous to believe!"

I grinned at both of them. "Miss me? I can't say I missed your cooking."

"The conquering hero," Barney said and reached out to shake my hand. Joe came from the griddle to do the same. I sat down.

"It's good to see you, Tom," Barney said more seriously, and Joe nodded.

Joe asked, "Have you looked up Jerry?"

I shook my head. There was a moment of uncomfortable silence.

Then Barney asked gently, "What'll it be, buddy?"

I started to answer as the door opened. It was Jerry. He stared at us as we stared at him, all of us too startled to say anything. Then he sat down quietly some distance from me and said, "A hamburger, please."

"Coming right up," Barney said and looked at me. "And you, Tom?"

It was a happy coincidence that I was facing the cereal boxes in neat rows behind the counter. Because there, among the corn flakes and bran flakes, the cereals that pop and those that crackle, in the middle of all those was the cereal Jerry and I knew well.

I said in a clear voice, "Barney, what I want most in the world is a great big bowl of Crispie Crunchies."

I was watching Jerry when he turned toward me and we must have stared at each other for seconds before he started to smile.

And he said, "Brothers, blood brothers. Man, I'm a creep, huh, Tom?"

"Not at the moment," I said. "Come on down here and sit, you sour loser!"

He came down to take the stool next to mine and it was like old times. I felt that a void in my life had been filled again. But through it all I couldn't help wondering how long this would last. Would it be like this *after* the Sagebrush?

If he won, it would.

He had a new Triumph, he told me, a real scrambler and both Bud and I would eat his dust today. Then Mr. Ellender came in, saw us together and said, "Well, it's about time. How are you, Tom?"

"Confident, sir," I said jokingly. "We hope to pick up a few dealers in that audience from Palm Springs."

"That new Tornado is certainly the talk of the trade," he admitted. "I wouldn't be surprised if they sold as well as Triumph in twenty or thirty years."

Barney said, "Charley, you'd better get on the bandwagon now. Remember how long you kept your money in that buggy-whip firm?"

They all laughed. It was a good time for laughing—*before* the race.

Then Ben and my dad pulled up in front and it was time for me to go. Jerry said, "I'll see you later. Say 'hello' to Bud for me."

"I'll be sure to," I promised him, and went out wondering how long this reasonable mood of Jerry Wilson's would last.

There were a lot of cars on the road to the course, cars with out-of-state license tags; the conventioneers were arriving early in order to find good vantage points to watch the race. Because of the change in date, this was going to be one of the best-attended Sagebrush Scrambles ever presented.

Bud was already in the pit area; he had come with Mr. Devlin. He was alone in the pit now, though, as Mr. Devlin was out circulating among the dealers who had already arrived. My dad went to join him.

I told Bud, "Jerry Wilson asked me to say 'hello' to you. I met him in the Dune Diner."

Bud sighed. "We're friends again, eh? For how long, Tom?"

I shrugged. "I've been wondering the same thing, myself. I hope it's for good. He has a new bike."

"I know," Bud said. "I've seen it. Add him to the list."

"What list?"

"The list of all the riders we have to worry about to-day," Bud answered. "Teammate, they're all here—Garvey and Dunn and Burke, Levy, Cady, Prentice. I'm *nervous*, man."

"We must learn to lose with grace," I parroted. "You should know the course. Didn't you finish forty-sixth in your first appearance here?"

"You're a funny fellow," he said acidly. "I hope you can keep your sense of humor alive all day. We're representing Temple, don't forget."

I was well aware of that. It was one of the reasons for the tension I shared with Bud. American Temple had taken a chance on us and we hadn't let them down too badly—yet. But today would be the most critical audience possible, men who were thinking of investing their money in a change of franchise.

Both my dad and Mr. Devlin were salesmen as well as engineers, but no sales talk is as effective as proof of quality through performance. Bud and I were the boys who had to prove that quality.

Ben Schulte must have sensed our moods. He said quietly, "I want you boys to think of this as a sport.

Remember, if you don't enjoy it you shouldn't be in it.
Go out to win, not to prove anything."

Bud grinned. "I just happen to have a commercial
bent. I had it long before today, Ben."

"You didn't get into this for the money in it," Ben
argued. "There never was that much money in it. Don't
try to fool me—you'd pay to ride here today."

And I remembered what my dad had said as we
waited to start the Pine Valley Run. He enjoyed his
work, now. That didn't show up in a bank account always but it was very important to him. And if some of
the great American success stories were checked
through, I'm sure that one factor would be predominant,
the impressive records were made by men who enjoyed
their work and respected their trades.

About five yards away, Red Dunn was unloading a
big, new Norton. Bud and I went over to help him.

"Stay away from me," he said lightly. "I'm suspicious
of your good will."

"You're a star," Bud said, winking at me. "We want
to get in good with the stars, so we can learn."

"You boys have learned," he said. "Too well." He
glanced over at our twin Tornadoes. "And now I hear
you've a pair of even hotter machines."

"We'll know before the sun goes down," I said. "This
Norton doesn't look second-hand to me."

"Take a good look at it," he told us. "Later, you'll
be able to watch my rear tire only." He patted the gas
tank. "This sweetheart is *ready*."

Then Johnny Burke was coming over and Bruce

Cady and some of the other boys to look at the Norton and our Tornadoes. Joking, friendly, all of them seeming to be much more confident than I felt or, I could guess, than Bud felt. Was it a front, this poise they had? Were they really as nervous as we were underneath?

When we were alone again, I asked Bud, "Didn't they seem less nervous than we are? Or didn't you notice it?"

He nodded. "I noticed it. They've had more experience than we have, Tom. And Ben's probably right— it's a sport. They're in it because they enjoy it." He grinned. "Let's start enjoying it. There's no reason for me to tighten; I'm not expected to do as well as you in this kind of racing."

"Thank you," I said and went over to help Ben.

The crowd grew larger and the day grew warmer. There would be no trial runs; it was a new course laid out here, and every entrant would start without previous knowledge. That could mean a slow first lap, except that these stars who were here had developed an almost instinctive knowledge of terrain and surface. They wouldn't be loafing so long as the route ahead was in sight.

The checkers were going out now to their stations but the crowd was not yet settled. The dealers were going from pit to pit, looking at all the new and racing-modified bikes; our Temples seemed to be drawing the largest audience.

The overcast was still keeping the direct heat of the

sun from us; it was a beautiful day for racing. Mr. Ellinder came over to talk with Ben; I went over to where Bud was getting a Coke out of the station wagon.

I fished one out of the cooler, too, and we stood there looking at the gray-green foothills and the long trail that led toward them, the start of the course.

"It's been changed, all right," he said. "It looks like it's going to skip that arroyo."

"Well," I guessed, "we won't be leading the parade. We can learn from following. We're riding the equipment, Bud, to have the edge."

"*You* have," he said. "I'm not sure it's enough edge for me, not against the boys here today. On a track, now—" He shrugged.

The line was forming; an assistant starter came over to give us our starting positions and numbers. We would start with engines running, a hundred bikes fighting for advantage on the trail that led through the sage.

The only stop check would be the finish-line check on each lap; the meet was staffed well enough to eliminate the need for others. With a hundred bikes to keep track of, that took *some* staff.

Engines running now, flanked on the left by a Norton, on the right by a Harley, I kept my eyes on the starter, clearly visible on his platform to the left of the long line. Eight bikes down that way, Jerry Wilson on his new Triumph waited and I wondered how confident *he* felt.

The flag was unfurled and raised as the engine bark grew sharper. It flashed down and bedlam took over. Both the Norton and the Harley shot past me as their drivers anticipated the flag better. Both the Norton and the Harley and how many others—? They all seemed to funnel past me as we jockeyed desperately through the sand to get to the harder surface of the trail. I was off to a bad start.

The trail now, and better going; there must have been three dozen bikes in front of me as I twisted the throttle to the limit and set sail.

It was a long, straight stretch to the first turn with plenty of room to pass. I managed to pass only two bikes as the others waged trail-wide fights for position, clotted in tangles of three and four, all hoping for a dust-free ride through the hills.

The first turn was abrupt, a left-hand turn that led into a small gully. Two bikes were already down here; the bike immediately ahead was coming into it too fast, I was sure.

I slowed and went down to third as he barreled into it at a ridiculous speed. It had been a wise move.

His rear wheel started to churn as he turned, throwing a cloud of sand. And then it hit hard clay—and he was out of control, gunning straight across the tight turn off the course. He would have to re-enter the course at the same spot; and with all those bikes coming up behind, that could cost him some lost seconds.

The Tornado went down into the turn, throwing a minimum of sand, and came out onto the better surface under full control. She was a winner, this new Tornado. Under Johnny Burke's hands, she would have taken this meet in a walk.

And under Tom Manning's? We would see, we would see. . . .

Into the gully, a graveled dry creek bed with no chance to pass for two hundred yards. I could see the whole single file of bikes ahead of me; there were too many. There was no point in counting them. Ben would give me my position at the finish-line check.

Up out of the gully in third, the Tornado's power leashed so we wouldn't climb all over the rear wheel of the laboring bike in front. Up, up and over the rim and into a wide, sloping run of clay and gravel. A twist of the wrist and the bike in front was now the bike behind.

We had made a gradual right turn in the gully; we were again heading toward the hills. Then ahead I saw the leading bike with both wheels off the ground, and realized the creek bed that had formed the gully had been a meandering stream. It was dry now, but its channel was still there and it crossed this trail as a hazard.

A downhill jump was not new to me, but a downhill jump with the far bank higher than the near bank was brand-new to me. I would have to keep that front wheel high.

If there was no take-off ramp, how could I do it? With a burst of power? How else? I watched the others.

Two of them didn't make it. The bike ahead of me moved faster as we approached and though I didn't know the rider, the sound of his machine convinced me he was no Johnny-come-lately. I decided to follow his technique.

Twenty yards short of the creek he slowed and went into third—and really gunned that Harley. Like a pilot coming in on radar, I followed his lead.

I had learned something new, new and valuable. The front end seemed to lift as I twisted the throttle; it was still lifting as we went over the creek and up the bank that climbed steeply around the spring-greem chaparral of the slope.

Up again, the power of the Temple reassuring, a small glimmer of confidence beginning to grow in me as we gained on the others climbing to the flat of the mesa.

It was dry up here and dusty. I had passed two cycles on the trip up; the machines ahead were moving too fast for me to risk a challenge now. I ate their dust and bided my time.

Ahead I could see a jump and the leading bike coming out of it and making a wide, sliding turn to the left that led downhill once more. In this dust, I wanted room for a jump. I let the bike ahead gain ground and looked behind to judge my clearance there.

Plenty of room, front and rear. I slowed very little, just enough to leave me some acceleration for take-off. The glimmer of new confidence was beginning to wane as the jump loomed closer.

Up, acceleration, the Tornado responding perfectly.

Soaring, landing cleanly and into the sliding left turn. And here it *almost* happened.

The traction had been so firm on the ramp I had almost lost my sense of surface. The rear wheel went sliding to the right as I fought it, leaning higher, conscious of the machine behind me now in the air and unable to change course.

My heart hammered, my left foot dug for support and braking as the rear continued to slide. Then, for a second, I felt the tug of regained traction and I took a chance on gunning out of it. I twisted for a spurt of power.

A lucky guess; we were once more upright and winging. Downhill on fine surface, the desert ahead below, the treacherous sand that could *never*, I felt sure, be traveled in high gear.

There were still far too many machines in front of me and I had been traveling very close to my personal limit. It was possible that the superiority of our new Temple Tornado wasn't enough edge to make up for the inferiority of rider Tom Manning.

Where, I wondered, was my old and new friend, Jerry Wilson? He had started to the left of me; a whole bank of riders from that side had reached the starting trail before me. It was a 90 per cent certainty that Jerry was in the group ahead.

A sharp right turn, a sharper left, another gully to get over, but this had a higher leading edge and a lip that acted as a ramp. Over it we sailed and onto the discarded road that ended a thousand yards ahead, ended in sand.

I stayed under full throttle, watching the leader, waiting to see when he shifted. Any man leading this parade, I reasoned, *must* know his trade.

He didn't shift!

The rains, the rains we'd had this spring. They had brought clay down from the mesa and this mixture had packed near the stream bed as the flash floods had overflowed the banks. The sand he was skimming over now was like Daytona when the tide went out.

How long would it last, as we left the flood area? I was glad to be back where I could watch the smart boys.

I kept one eye on the leader, one on the competition immediately ahead. Lacking a third eye, I had no chance to check the possible challengers from behind. I *had* to see when the leader shifted.

He didn't shift until his Spitfire was about four hundred yards from the starting line. There was a cactus almost abreast of him when he shifted; I decided to use it as my marker.

It worked all right. I didn't gain on any of the bikes ahead, but I didn't lose ground, either. The Tornado plowed through steadily in third and, so far as I could tell, there was no firmer ground on either side of me.

And now we were rolling down on the stop check and, twenty feet short of the line, Ben had the slate held high with a huge "28" chalked on it. That meant I was finishing the first lap in twenty-eighth place.

Twenty-seven ahead of me and nine laps to go. It

didn't seem impossible, but the twenty-seven ahead had been maintaining their gap and I had been driving very close to my limit.

I was twenty-seventh two minutes later. A Cliburn Comet ahead of me threw a big end bearing on the hard, curving sweep toward the gully, and almost dumped the rider into a cactus.

On this uphill going, my bike had plenty of power left. It seemed logical to me that if I was going to improve, I couldn't pick a better place than here and now. The trail was wide and there would be dust ahead.

I stayed in high and went to full throttle. We were past the BMW ahead before its rider realized he was being challenged. Ahead of him was Ron Stiles on a Matchless, and Ron wasn't ready to make any move as yet. We went past him before the dip and the sandy turn; we went through that under full throttle in third gear, and almost rammed into a Triumph slowing for the gully entrance.

I felt an exhilaration that had been lacking in my first exploratory round; my mood was almost a match for the Tornado's eager potential. She chattered impatiently as we threaded the gully, as though annoyed at the need for single-file travel.

Out of it and past the Triumph as we sped over the hard clay toward the downhill creek crossing. One bike was down here; we went over without jar and started the climb to the mesa.

I must have passed some bikes that were down without seeing them on that lap. Because I figured my position to be twenty-third as we churned through the sand to the second stop check.

But Ben had a "20" on the slate held high in both hands. My dad, standing next to him, held a clenched fist aloft in encouragement. Twentieth place—I owed him something better than that, riding this dream of his.

I gave the Tornado a better ride on her next trip. I've forgotten now how many places I climbed; all I remember is that I was finally up with the boys who were going to make any further advance much more difficult.

I wasn't fool enough to think my skill matched theirs. I could hope the combination of Devlin-Manning engineering and Ben Schulte tuning gave me an advantage strong enough to overcome my lacks.

That was only a hope; a calculated judgment, based on hope. I needed an impetus stronger than that to match the pace these hot-foots were setting.

I found the impetus in the seventh lap, finally. It was a lad on a new Triumph whose skill alone might not have put him where he was, but whose skill and imagination and *competitive spirit* had him here with the giants.

He was a lad I knew with a spirit I needed. He was Jerry Wilson.

I caught him coming out of the gully when he was giving all of his attention to the gravel surface that was beginning to come loose from the clay.

I went past him fifty yards short of the climb to the

mesa, coming up on his left side as he was looking back to the right. He didn't even see me until I was past him.

I guess you would have to say that Jerry Wilson was completely responsible for what happened in the last three and a half laps of that Sagebrush Scrambles.

Ten seconds after I had passed him, he was climbing up on my right, crowding me as we sped across the flat, fast going of the mesa. If it had been anybod·ⁿ else, I might have resisted the challenge. But who is more competitive than a friend?

I took off and he followed like an avenging angel, forcing me to milk the last potential mile an hour out of the Tornado as we came streaking toward the jump.

At this speed, I would wind up on the moon. And a year ago, I was sure, Jerry would have crowded me into such a calamitous move. Today, his Triumph slowed, giving me clearance to jump alone.

He had learned to drive with discipline, it was clear. Had he also learned to lose with grace? At the moment, my chances of discovering that weren't too bright. How long could I keep ahead of a rider as determined as he was?

On the slope down, we passed Jack Pardee and moved past Ed Garvey on the old road that led to the sand. We were moving at a speed I would never have attempted alone, and it seemed to me that Jerry's Triumph had a higher top speed; I had the edge in off-road traction. I filed that for possible future use.

He gained on the road; he lost it again in the deeper sand near the finish line. I checked in ahead of him and checked out in my shortest stop of the race. Ben's slate had informed me I was in fifth place.

That put Jerry in sixth and put the real cream of the meet ahead of us. Because at the rate we were moving, only the top riders would still be in front. Without Jerry's challenge, I wouldn't have been this high.

The challenge didn't desert me. He stayed close as a sand burr, haunting me, egging me on, giving me no rest, forcing me to handle that solid Tornado at the absolute peak of my ability.

The Tornado took it; I almost didn't. A challenge as constant and determined as Jerry's was a heavy strain on my nerves. I had the feeling that if I made even a minor mistake in judgment or handling, he would not only pass, but it could be disastrous for me. I had a strong urge to slow down and let him go past.

We had learned together. My pride was involved. If it had been Johnny Burke or Red Dunn, there would be reason for me to slow down. But Jerry's experience was no greater than mine and his machine no more ready. I didn't quit.

In that first homemade scrambles course we had laid out on the desert, hadn't I bettered his time on our antique Harley? Had he learned more than I had since? My pride wouldn't permit me to admit that.

The gully, the climb, the mesa, the jump—they moved by in a blur and we passed a bike I didn't recognize and again it seemed to me Jerry was gaining on the road, losing out again in the soft sand near the line.

It was a war of nerves, the way he crowded me, wait-

ing for the wrong move from me, the chance to go by
and go after the leaders. But at the finish of the ninth
lap, neither of us had to worry about the leaders.

I was in first place, Jerry in second.

It would be nice to relate how easily I beat him, how
I put on a spectacular show for that final screaming
lap and won by two hundred yards, going away.

It wouldn't be true. Because he finally caught me.
Through more than three-quarters of that last lap, I
successfully fought off each of the half-dozen chal-
lenges he made, and I thought I had fought off the last
one as I made the final creek passage luckier than he
had and came charging onto the firm surface.

Above the whine of our machines I could hear the
crowd yelling encouragement to both of us, and the
confidence I had been seeking all day finally welled
through me.

This one, I thought, *is a win for American Temple,
and all dealers present please take notice.*

This one, I thought—and thought no more. Jerry
Wilson had flashed past me as my confidence reached
its peak.

I was wide open on this deserted road, wide open and
completely frustrated. The Tornado was revving at her
limit—and the Triumph was moving away from us.

It is always the combination that wins, the man *and*
the machine; Jerry's machine had more speed on firm,
flat going. Jerry's skill had put him into position where
that particular superiority of his machine could be used
to final advantage.

It was going to be a hard race to lose.

If I lost.

It seemed lost to me. Though I expected to gain again in the soft and now rutted sand, it seemed unlikely that I would gain back all the ground he was gaining on this level blacktop.

And then, as we moved through the screams of the spectators, as the end of the road dropped behind and we were on the still-packed sand of the desert, I decided to take a chance.

I had tried it, long ago, on that ancient Harley, and it had given me the thirty-four-second lap that Jerry had lied about. I had stayed in high gear, tried to keep the front wheel up, and skimmed over the sand that hadn't been disturbed by Jerry's previous trips. It might be a bad risk, but I was sure the technique of my first nine laps wasn't good enough for this last-lap challenge.

I saw Jerry go into third as he came abreast of the lone cactus; I took a deep breath and stayed in high two seconds later. I couldn't keep an eye on him and watch the treacherous surface ahead; I stayed with my problem and let Jerry solve his own. Underneath the upper, wind-loosened sand, there should still be some firm surface from the recent rains. It worked for the first hundred yards, at any rate.

Ahead, the going looked firm enough and I finally stole a glance to my left, where Jerry was choosing a different course and a more thoroughly tested technique.

I was gaining on him!

I had expected to gain, but I was gaining more, I knew, than I had expected to gain in third gear.

And now Jerry looked back and must have known by the diminished sound of my machine that I had never gone down to third gear. And Jerry took a chance of his own.

He, too, decided to try top gear.

I didn't look; I was too busy watching the path ahead, too tense because I intended to add a few horses to the Tornado's steady pull.

If what I expected to happen to Jerry did happen, I wouldn't have to see it; I would be able to hear it.

I heard it.

He went to high, engaged the clutch, and didn't slow his engine enough to maintain the same tractive speed. His engine pitch rose as his rear wheel began to channel a furrow in the soft sand—and he went desperately back to third, compounding the error.

Lightly, the Temple skimmed over the surface, lightly, easily, carefully, delicately—and *successfully*.

Into first place we danced, as the sound of Jerry's engine grew less wild, as he began to find traction, pick up speed.

The crowd was quieter; they had shouted themselves hoarse, and this precarious game of traction at reduced speed was more like a chess game than a motorcycle race.

Ahead was the checkered flag and I wanted to look back, wanted to make sure this race was won, but there was sand ahead that appeared even more treacherous than the passage had been so far.

I kept my eyes on the front wheel and my hopes on the checkered flag. I didn't look back until it had flashed for me.

And as I looked back, I thought of Ben Schulte's prophecy that no matter how painful it might be, Jerry Wilson *would* learn. He was only fifteen feet behind me as the flag flashed. He had picked up thirty feet in the last fifty, I learned later.

And then my dad was hugging me and Ben Schulte was calling me "champ" and the fans were crowding around and Mr. Devlin was smiling as though he had just discovered oil.

It was a great day for all of us, but I kept looking around, waiting for the man who would make it even greater.

And finally he came shouldering through the crowd and though his grin was a sad effort, it was a grin and his hand was out in congratulations.

Jerry Wilson, best friend and unrelenting competitor, had finally learned the hard way to be something equally important—a gracious loser.

About William Campbell Gault

William Campbell Gault was born in Milwaukee, Wisconsin, and lived there until 1950 when he moved to California. He now calls Santa Barbara his home. During World War II he served in Texas with the 166th Infantry and in Hawaii with the 13th Replacement Depot.

Mr. Gault is a full-time professional writer, but he has been an iceman, mailman, aircraft assembler, bus boy, waiter and manager of a hotel. He devotes his spare time to his wife and two children, a new home, and golf.

He is well-known to mystery fans. His previous books for young people are: *Gallant Colt, Mr. Fullback, Mr. Quarterback, Bruce Benedict—Halfback, Dim Thunder, Drag Strip, Rough Road to Glory, Speedway Challenge, Thunder Road, Dirt Track Summer,* and *Through the Line.*